Conversion Factors

DIMENSION	METRIC	METRIC/ENGLISH
Acceleration	$1 \text{ m/s}^2 = 100 \text{ cm/s}^2$	$1 \text{ m/s}^2 =$ ▯▯▯▯▯▯ $1 \text{ ft/s}^2 =$
Area	$1 \text{ m}^2 = 10^4 \text{ cm}^2 = 10^6 \text{ mm}^2 = 10^{-6} \text{ km}^2$	$1 \text{ m}^2 =$ $1 \text{ ft}^2 =$
Density	$1 \text{ g/cm}^3 = 1 \text{ kg/L} = 1000 \text{ kg/m}^3$	$1 \text{ g/cm}^3 =$ ░░░░ lbm/ft $= 0.036127$ lbm/in^3 $1 \text{ lbm/in}^3 = 1728 \text{ lbm/ft}^3$ $1 \text{ kg/m}^3 = 0.062428 \text{ lbm/ft}^3$
Energy, heat, work, internal energy, enthalpy	$1 \text{ kJ} = 1000 \text{ J} = 1000 \text{ N} \cdot \text{m} = 1 \text{ kPa} \cdot \text{m}^3$ $1 \text{ kJ/kg} = 1000 \text{ m}^2/\text{s}^2$ $1 \text{ kWh} = 3600 \text{ kJ}$ $1 \text{ cal}^\dagger = 4.184 \text{ J}$ $1 \text{ IT cal}^\dagger = 4.1868 \text{ J}$ $1 \text{ Cal}^\dagger = 4.1868 \text{ kJ}$	$1 \text{ kJ} = 0.94782 \text{ Btu}$ $1 \text{ Btu} = 1.055056 \text{ kJ}$ $\quad = 5.40395 \text{ psia} \cdot \text{ft}^3 = 778.169 \text{ lbf} \cdot \text{ft}$ $1 \text{ Btu/lbm} = 25{,}037 \text{ ft}^2/\text{s}^2 = 2.326^* \text{ kJ/kg}$ $1 \text{ kJ/kg} = 0.430 \text{ Btu/lbm}$ $1 \text{ kWh} = 3412.14 \text{ Btu}$ $1 \text{ therm} = 10^5 \text{ Btu} = 1.055 \times 10^5 \text{ kJ}$ (natural gas)
Force	$1 \text{ N} = 1 \text{ kg} \cdot \text{m/s}^2 = 10^5 \text{ dyne}$ $1 \text{ kgf} = 9.80665 \text{ N}$	$1 \text{ N} = 0.22481 \text{ lbf}$ $1 \text{ lbf} = 32.174 \text{ lbm} \cdot \text{ft/s}^2 = 4.44822 \text{ N}$
Heat flux	$1 \text{ W/cm}^2 = 10^4 \text{ W/m}^2$	$1 \text{ W/m}^2 = 0.3171 \text{ Btu/h} \cdot \text{ft}^2$
Heat transfer coefficient	$1 \text{ W/m}^2 \cdot {}^\circ\text{C} = 1 \text{ W/m}^2 \cdot \text{K}$	$1 \text{ W/m}^2 \cdot {}^\circ\text{C} = 0.17612 \text{ Btu/h} \cdot \text{ft}^2 \cdot {}^\circ\text{F}$
Length	$1 \text{ m} = 100 \text{ cm} = 1000 \text{ mm} = 10^6 \text{ } \mu\text{m}$ $1 \text{ km} = 1000 \text{ m}$	$1 \text{ m} = 39.370 \text{ in} = 3.2808 \text{ ft} = 1.0926 \text{ yd}$ $1 \text{ ft} = 12 \text{ in} = 0.3048^* \text{ m}$ $1 \text{ mile} = 5280 \text{ ft} = 1.6093 \text{ km}$ $1 \text{ in} = 2.54^* \text{ cm}$
Mass	$1 \text{ kg} = 1000 \text{ g}$ $1 \text{ metric ton} = 1000 \text{ kg}$	$1 \text{ kg} = 2.2046226 \text{ lbm}$ $1 \text{ lbm} = 0.45359237^* \text{ kg}$ $1 \text{ ounce} = 28.3495 \text{ g}$ $1 \text{ slug} = 32.174 \text{ lbm} = 14.5939 \text{ kg}$ $1 \text{ short ton} = 2000 \text{ lbm} = 907.1847 \text{ kg}$
Power, heat transfer rate	$1 \text{ W} = 1 \text{ J/s}$ $1 \text{ kW} = 1000 \text{ W} = 1.341 \text{ hp}$ $1 \text{ hp}^\ddagger = 745.7 \text{ W}$	$1 \text{ kW} = 3412.14 \text{ Btu/h}$ $\quad = 737.56 \text{ lbf} \cdot \text{ft/s}$ $1 \text{ hp} = 550 \text{ lbf} \cdot \text{ft/s} = 0.7068 \text{ Btu/s}$ $\quad = 42.41 \text{ Btu/min} = 2544.5 \text{ Btu/h}$ $\quad = 0.74570 \text{ kW}$ $1 \text{ boiler hp} = 33{,}475 \text{ Btu/h}$ $1 \text{ Btu/h} = 1.055056 \text{ kJ/h}$ $1 \text{ ton of refrigeration} = 200 \text{ Btu/min}$
Pressure	$1 \text{ Pa} = 1 \text{ N/m}^2$ $1 \text{ kPa} = 10^3 \text{ Pa} = 10^{-3} \text{ MPa}$ $1 \text{ atm} = 101.325 \text{ kPa} = 1.01325 \text{ bars}$ $\quad = 760 \text{ mm Hg at } 0{}^\circ\text{C}$ $\quad = 1.03323 \text{ kgf/cm}^2$ $1 \text{ mm Hg} = 0.1333 \text{ kPa}$	$1 \text{ Pa} = 1.4504 \times 10^{-4} \text{ psia}$ $\quad = 0.020886 \text{ lbf/ft}^2$ $1 \text{ psi} = 144 \text{ lbf/ft}^2 = 6.894757 \text{ kPa}$ $1 \text{ atm} = 14.696 \text{ psia} = 29.92 \text{ in Hg at } 30{}^\circ\text{F}$ $1 \text{ in Hg} = 3.387 \text{ kPa}$
Specific heat	$1 \text{ kJ/kg} \cdot {}^\circ\text{C} = 1 \text{ kJ/kg} \cdot \text{K} = 1 \text{ J/g} \cdot {}^\circ\text{C}$	$1 \text{ Btu/lbm} \cdot {}^\circ\text{F} = 4.1868 \text{ kJ/kg} \cdot {}^\circ\text{C}$ $1 \text{ Btu/lbmol} \cdot \text{R} = 4.1868 \text{ kJ/kmol} \cdot \text{K}$ $1 \text{ kJ/kg} \cdot {}^\circ\text{C} = 0.23885 \text{ Btu/lbm} \cdot {}^\circ\text{F}$ $\quad = 0.23885 \text{ Btu/lbm} \cdot \text{R}$

*Exact conversion factor between metric and English units.

†Calorie is originally defined as the amount of heat needed to raise the temperature of 1 g of water by 1°C, but it varies with temperature. The international steam table (IT) calorie (generally preferred by engineers) is exactly 4.1868 J by definition and corresponds to the specific heat of water at 15°C. The thermochemical calorie (generally preferred by physicists) is exactly 4.184 J by definition and corresponds to the specific heat of water at room temperature. The difference between the two is about 0.06 percent, which is negligible. The capitalized Calorie used by nutritionists is actually a kilocalorie (1000 IT calories).

DIMENSION	METRIC	METRIC/ENGLISH
Specific volume	$1\ m^3/kg = 1000\ L/kg = 1000\ cm^3/g$	$1\ m^3/kg = 16.02\ ft^3/lbm$ $1\ ft^3/lbm = 0.062428\ m^3/kg$
Temperature	$T(K) = T(°C) + 273.15$ $\Delta T(K) = \Delta T(°C)$	$T(R) = T(°F) + 459.67 = 1.8\,T(K)$ $T(°F) = 1.8\ T(°C) + 32$ $\Delta T(°F) = \Delta T(R) = 1.8\ \Delta T(K)$
Thermal conductivity	$1\ W/m \cdot °C = 1\ W/m \cdot K$	$1\ W/m \cdot °C = 0.57782\ Btu/h \cdot ft \cdot °F$
Velocity	$1\ m/s = 3.60\ km/h$	$1\ m/s = 3.2808\ ft/s = 2.237\ mi/h$ $1\ mi/h = 1.46667\ ft/s$ $1\ mi/h = 1.6093\ km/h$
Volume	$1\ m^3 = 1000\ L = 10^6\ cm^3\ (cc)$	$1\ m^3 = 6.1024 \times 10^4\ in^3 = 35.315\ ft^3$ $\quad = 264.17\ gal\ (U.S.)$ $1\ U.S.\ gallon = 231\ in^3 = 3.7854\ L$ $1\ fl\ ounce = 29.5735\ cm^3 = 0.0295735\ L$ $1\ U.S.\ gallon = 128\ fl\ ounces$
Volume flow rate	$1\ m^3/s = 60,000\ L/min = 10^6\ cm^3/s$	$1\ m^3/s = 15,850\ gal/min\ (gpm) = 35.315\ ft^3/s$ $\quad = 2118.9\ ft^3/min\ (cfm)$

‡Mechanical horsepower. The electrical horsepower is taken to be exactly 746 W.

Some Physical Constants

Universal gas constant	$R_u = 8.31447\ kJ/kmol \cdot K$ $\quad = 8.31447\ kPa \cdot m^3/kmol \cdot K$ $\quad = 0.0831447\ bar \cdot m^3/kmol \cdot K$ $\quad = 82.05\ L \cdot atm/kmol \cdot K$ $\quad = 1.9858\ Btu/lbmol \cdot R$ $\quad = 1545.37\ ft \cdot lbf/lbmol \cdot R$ $\quad = 10.73\ psia \cdot ft^3/lbmol \cdot R$
Standard acceleration of gravity	$g = 9.80665\ m/s^2$ $\quad = 32.174\ ft/s^2$
Standard atmospheric pressure	$1\ atm = 101.325\ kPa$ $\quad = 1.01325\ bar$ $\quad = 14.696\ psia$ $\quad = 760\ mm\ Hg\ (0°C)$ $\quad = 29.9213\ in\ Hg\ (32°F)$ $\quad = 10.3323\ m\ H_2O\ (4°C)$
Stefan–Boltzmann constant	$\sigma = 5.6704 \times 10^{-8}\ W/m^2 \cdot K^4$ $\quad = 0.1714 \times 10^{-8}\ Btu/h \cdot ft^2 \cdot R^4$
Boltzmann's constant	$k = 1.380650 \times 10^{-23}\ J/K$
Speed of light in vacuum	$c_o = 2.9979 \times 10^8\ m/s$ $\quad = 9.836 \times 10^8\ ft/s$
Speed of sound in dry air at 0°C and 1 atm	$c = 331.36\ m/s$ $\quad = 1089\ ft/s$
Heat of fusion of water at 1 atm	$h_{if} = 333.7\ kJ/kg$ $\quad = 143.5\ Btu/lbm$
Enthalpy of vaporization of water at 1 atm	$h_{fg} = 2256.5\ kJ/kg$ $\quad = 970.12\ Btu/lbm$

Property Tables Booklet

for use with

THERMODYNAMICS

An Engineering Approach

FIFTH EDITION

YUNUS A. ÇENGEL

University of Nevada, Reno

MICHAEL A. BOLES

North Carolina State University

Boston   Burr Ridge, IL   Dubuque, IA   Madison, WI   New York   San Francisco   St. Louis
Bangkok   Bogotá   Caracas   Kuala Lumpur   Lisbon   London   Madrid   Mexico City
Milan   Montreal   New Delhi   Santiago   Seoul   Singapore   Sydney   Taipei   Toronto

McGraw-Hill Higher Education

*A Division of The **McGraw-Hill** Companies*

Property Tables Booklet for use with
THERMODYNAMICS: AN ENGINEERING APPROACH, FIFTH EDITION
YUNUS A. ÇENGEL AND MICHAEL A. BOLES

Published by McGraw-Hill Higher Education, an imprint of The McGraw-Hill Companies, Inc., 1221 Avenue of the Americas, New York, NY 10020. Copyright © The McGraw-Hill Companies, Inc., 2006, 2002, 1998, 1994, 1989. All rights reserved.

This book is printed on acid-free paper.

1 2 3 4 5 6 7 8 9 0 QPD/QPD 0 9 8 7 6 5

ISBN 0-07-288497-5

www.mhhe.com

Appendix 1

PROPERTY TABLES AND CHARTS (SI UNITS)

Molar mass, gas constant, and critical-point properties

Substance	Formula	Molar mass, M kg/kmol	Gas constant, R kJ/kg · K*	Critical-point properties		
				Temperature, K	Pressure, MPa	Volume, m^3/kmol
Air	—	28.97	0.2870	132.5	3.77	0.0883
Ammonia	NH_3	17.03	0.4882	405.5	11.28	0.0724
Argon	Ar	39.948	0.2081	151	4.86	0.0749
Benzene	C_6H_6	78.115	0.1064	562	4.92	0.2603
Bromine	Br_2	159.808	0.0520	584	10.34	0.1355
n-Butane	C_4H_{10}	58.124	0.1430	425.2	3.80	0.2547
Carbon dioxide	CO_2	44.01	0.1889	304.2	7.39	0.0943
Carbon monoxide	CO	28.011	0.2968	133	3.50	0.0930
Carbon tetrachloride	CCl_4	153.82	0.05405	556.4	4.56	0.2759
Chlorine	Cl_2	70.906	0.1173	417	7.71	0.1242
Chloroform	$CHCl_3$	119.38	0.06964	536.6	5.47	0.2403
Dichlorodifluoromethane (R-12)	CCl_2F_2	120.91	0.06876	384.7	4.01	0.2179
Dichlorofluoromethane (R-21)	$CHCl_2F$	102.92	0.08078	451.7	5.17	0.1973
Ethane	C_2H_6	30.070	0.2765	305.5	4.48	0.1480
Ethyl alcohol	C_2H_5OH	46.07	0.1805	516	6.38	0.1673
Ethylene	C_2H_4	28.054	0.2964	282.4	5.12	0.1242
Helium	He	4.003	2.0769	5.3	0.23	0.0578
n-Hexane	C_6H_{14}	86.179	0.09647	507.9	3.03	0.3677
Hydrogen (normal)	H_2	2.016	4.1240	33.3	1.30	0.0649
Krypton	Kr	83.80	0.09921	209.4	5.50	0.0924
Methane	CH_4	16.043	0.5182	191.1	4.64	0.0993
Methyl alcohol	CH_3OH	32.042	0.2595	513.2	7.95	0.1180
Methyl chloride	CH_3Cl	50.488	0.1647	416.3	6.68	0.1430
Neon	Ne	20.183	0.4119	44.5	2.73	0.0417
Nitrogen	N_2	28.013	0.2968	126.2	3.39	0.0899
Nitrous oxide	N_2O	44.013	0.1889	309.7	7.27	0.0961
Oxygen	O_2	31.999	0.2598	154.8	5.08	0.0780
Propane	C_3H_8	44.097	0.1885	370	4.26	0.1998
Propylene	C_3H_6	42.081	0.1976	365	4.62	0.1810
Sulfur dioxide	SO_2	64.063	0.1298	430.7	7.88	0.1217
Tetrafluoroethane (R-134a)	CF_3CH_2F	102.03	0.08149	374.2	4.059	0.1993
Trichlorofluoromethane (R-11)	CCl_3F	137.37	0.06052	471.2	4.38	0.2478
Water	H_2O	18.015	0.4615	647.1	22.06	0.0560
Xenon	Xe	131.30	0.06332	289.8	5.88	0.1186

*The unit kJ/kg · K is equivalent to kPa · m^3/kg · K. The gas constant is calculated from $R = R_u/M$, where $R_u = 8.31447$ kJ/kmol · K and M is the molar mass.

Source: K. A. Kobe and R. E. Lynn, Jr., Chemical Review 52 (1953), pp. 117–236; and ASHRAE, Handbook of Fundamentals (Atlanta, GA: American Society of Heating, Refrigerating and Air-Conditioning Engineers, Inc., 1993), pp. 16.4 and 36.1.

TABLE A–2

Ideal-gas specific heats of various common gases

(a) At 300 K

Gas	Formula	Gas constant, R kJ/kg · K	c_p kJ/kg · K	c_v kJ/kg · K	k
Air	—	0.2870	1.005	0.718	1.400
Argon	Ar	0.2081	0.5203	0.3122	1.667
Butane	C_4H_{10}	0.1433	1.7164	1.5734	1.091
Carbon dioxide	CO_2	0.1889	0.846	0.657	1.289
Carbon monoxide	CO	0.2968	1.040	0.744	1.400
Ethane	C_2H_6	0.2765	1.7662	1.4897	1.186
Ethylene	C_2H_4	0.2964	1.5482	1.2518	1.237
Helium	He	2.0769	5.1926	3.1156	1.667
Hydrogen	H_2	4.1240	14.307	10.183	1.405
Methane	CH_4	0.5182	2.2537	1.7354	1.299
Neon	Ne	0.4119	1.0299	0.6179	1.667
Nitrogen	N_2	0.2968	1.039	0.743	1.400
Octane	C_8H_{18}	0.0729	1.7113	1.6385	1.044
Oxygen	O_2	0.2598	0.918	0.658	1.395
Propane	C_3H_8	0.1885	1.6794	1.4909	1.126
Steam	H_2O	0.4615	1.8723	1.4108	1.327

Note: The unit kJ/kg · K is equivalent to kJ/kg · °C.
Source: Chemical and Process Thermodynamics 3/E by Kyle, B. G., © 2000. Adapted by permission of Pearson Education, Inc., Upper Saddle River, NJ.

(b) At various temperatures

Temperature, K	c_p kJ/kg · K	c_v kJ/kg · K	k	c_p kJ/kg · K	c_v kJ/kg · K	k	c_p kJ/kg · K	c_v kJ/kg · K	k
	Air			*Carbon dioxide, CO_2*			*Carbon monoxide, CO*		
250	1.003	0.716	1.401	0.791	0.602	1.314	1.039	0.743	1.400
300	1.005	0.718	1.400	0.846	0.657	1.288	1.040	0.744	1.399
350	1.008	0.721	1.398	0.895	0.706	1.268	1.043	0.746	1.398
400	1.013	0.726	1.395	0.939	0.750	1.252	1.047	0.751	1.395
450	1.020	0.733	1.391	0.978	0.790	1.239	1.054	0.757	1.392
500	1.029	0.742	1.387	1.014	0.825	1.229	1.063	0.767	1.387
550	1.040	0.753	1.381	1.046	0.857	1.220	1.075	0.778	1.382
600	1.051	0.764	1.376	1.075	0.886	1.213	1.087	0.790	1.376
650	1.063	0.776	1.370	1.102	0.913	1.207	1.100	0.803	1.370
700	1.075	0.788	1.364	1.126	0.937	1.202	1.113	0.816	1.364
750	1.087	0.800	1.359	1.148	0.959	1.197	1.126	0.829	1.358
800	1.099	0.812	1.354	1.169	0.980	1.193	1.139	0.842	1.353
900	1.121	0.834	1.344	1.204	1.015	1.186	1.163	0.866	1.343
1000	1.142	0.855	1.336	1.234	1.045	1.181	1.185	0.888	1.335
	Hydrogen, H_2			*Nitrogen, N_2*			*Oxygen, O_2*		
250	14.051	9.927	1.416	1.039	0.742	1.400	0.913	0.653	1.398
300	14.307	10.183	1.405	1.039	0.743	1.400	0.918	0.658	1.395
350	14.427	10.302	1.400	1.041	0.744	1.399	0.928	0.668	1.389
400	14.476	10.352	1.398	1.044	0.747	1.397	0.941	0.681	1.382
450	14.501	10.377	1.398	1.049	0.752	1.395	0.956	0.696	1.373
500	14.513	10.389	1.397	1.056	0.759	1.391	0.972	0.712	1.365
550	14.530	10.405	1.396	1.065	0.768	1.387	0.988	0.728	1.358
600	14.546	10.422	1.396	1.075	0.778	1.382	1.003	0.743	1.350
650	14.571	10.447	1.395	1.086	0.789	1.376	1.017	0.758	1.343
700	14.604	10.480	1.394	1.098	0.801	1.371	1.031	0.771	1.337
750	14.645	10.521	1.392	1.110	0.813	1.365	1.043	0.783	1.332
800	14.695	10.570	1.390	1.121	0.825	1.360	1.054	0.794	1.327
900	14.822	10.698	1.385	1.145	0.849	1.349	1.074	0.814	1.319
1000	14.983	10.859	1.380	1.167	0.870	1.341	1.090	0.830	1.313

Source: Kenneth Wark, *Thermodynamics,* 4th ed. (New York: McGraw-Hill, 1983), p. 783, Table A–4M. Originally published in *Tables of Thermal Properties of Gases,* NBS Circular 564, 1955.

TABLE A–2

Ideal-gas specific heats of various common gases (*Concluded*)

(*c*) As a function of temperature

$$\overline{c}_p = a + bT + cT^2 + dT^3$$

(T in K, c_p in kJ/kmol · K)

Substance	Formula	a	b	c	d	Temperature range, K	% error Max.	% error Avg.
Nitrogen	N_2	28.90	-0.1571×10^{-2}	0.8081×10^{-5}	-2.873×10^{-9}	273–1800	0.59	0.34
Oxygen	O_2	25.48	1.520×10^{-2}	-0.7155×10^{-5}	1.312×10^{-9}	273–1800	1.19	0.28
Air	—	28.11	0.1967×10^{-2}	0.4802×10^{-5}	-1.966×10^{-9}	273–1800	0.72	0.33
Hydrogen	H_2	29.11	-0.1916×10^{-2}	0.4003×10^{-5}	-0.8704×10^{-9}	273–1800	1.01	0.26
Carbon monoxide	CO	28.16	0.1675×10^{-2}	0.5372×10^{-5}	-2.222×10^{-9}	273–1800	0.89	0.37
Carbon dioxide	CO_2	22.26	5.981×10^{-2}	-3.501×10^{-5}	7.469×10^{-9}	273–1800	0.67	0.22
Water vapor	H_2O	32.24	0.1923×10^{-2}	1.055×10^{-5}	-3.595×10^{-9}	273–1800	0.53	0.24
Nitric oxide	NO	29.34	-0.09395×10^{-2}	0.9747×10^{-5}	-4.187×10^{-9}	273–1500	0.97	0.36
Nitrous oxide	N_2O	24.11	5.8632×10^{-2}	-3.562×10^{-5}	10.58×10^{-9}	273–1500	0.59	0.26
Nitrogen dioxide	NO_2	22.9	5.715×10^{-2}	-3.52×10^{-5}	7.87×10^{-9}	273–1500	0.46	0.18
Ammonia	NH_3	27.568	2.5630×10^{-2}	0.99072×10^{-5}	-6.6909×10^{-9}	273–1500	0.91	0.36
Sulfur	S_2	27.21	2.218×10^{-2}	-1.628×10^{-5}	3.986×10^{-9}	273–1800	0.99	0.38
Sulfur dioxide	SO_2	25.78	5.795×10^{-2}	-3.812×10^{-5}	8.612×10^{-9}	273–1800	0.45	0.24
Sulfur trioxide	SO_3	16.40	14.58×10^{-2}	-11.20×10^{-5}	32.42×10^{-9}	273–1300	0.29	0.13
Acetylene	C_2H_2	21.8	9.2143×10^{-2}	-6.527×10^{-5}	18.21×10^{-9}	273–1500	1.46	0.59
Benzene	C_6H_6	-36.22	48.475×10^{-2}	-31.57×10^{-5}	77.62×10^{-9}	273–1500	0.34	0.20
Methanol	CH_4O	19.0	9.152×10^{-2}	-1.22×10^{-5}	-8.039×10^{-9}	273–1000	0.18	0.08
Ethanol	C_2H_6O	19.9	20.96×10^{-2}	-10.38×10^{-5}	20.05×10^{-9}	273–1500	0.40	0.22
Hydrogen chloride	HCl	30.33	-0.7620×10^{-2}	1.327×10^{-5}	-4.338×10^{-9}	273–1500	0.22	0.08
Methane	CH_4	19.89	5.024×10^{-2}	1.269×10^{-5}	-11.01×10^{-9}	273–1500	1.33	0.57
Ethane	C_2H_6	6.900	17.27×10^{-2}	-6.406×10^{-5}	7.285×10^{-9}	273–1500	0.83	0.28
Propane	C_3H_8	-4.04	30.48×10^{-2}	-15.72×10^{-5}	31.74×10^{-9}	273–1500	0.40	0.12
n-Butane	C_4H_{10}	3.96	37.15×10^{-2}	-18.34×10^{-5}	35.00×10^{-9}	273–1500	0.54	0.24
i-Butane	C_4H_{10}	-7.913	41.60×10^{-2}	-23.01×10^{-5}	49.91×10^{-9}	273–1500	0.25	0.13
n-Pentane	C_5H_{12}	6.774	45.43×10^{-2}	-22.46×10^{-5}	42.29×10^{-9}	273–1500	0.56	0.21
n-Hexane	C_6H_{14}	6.938	55.22×10^{-2}	-28.65×10^{-5}	57.69×10^{-9}	273–1500	0.72	0.20
Ethylene	C_2H_4	3.95	15.64×10^{-2}	-8.344×10^{-5}	17.67×10^{-9}	273–1500	0.54	0.13
Propylene	C_3H_6	3.15	23.83×10^{-2}	-12.18×10^{-5}	24.62×10^{-9}	273–1500	0.73	0.17

Source: B. G. Kyle, *Chemical and Process Thermodynamics* (Englewood Cliffs, NJ: Prentice-Hall, 1984). Used with permission.

TABLE A–3

Properties of common liquids, solids, and foods

(a) Liquids

Substance	Boiling data at 1 atm		Freezing data		Liquid properties		
	Normal boiling point, °C	Latent heat of vaporization h_{fg}, kJ/kg	Freezing point, °C	Latent heat of fusion h_{if}, kJ/kg	Temperature, °C	Density ρ, kg/m³	Specific heat c_p, kJ/kg · K
Ammonia	−33.3	1357	−77.7	322.4	−33.3	682	4.43
					−20	665	4.52
					0	639	4.60
					25	602	4.80
Argon	−185.9	161.6	−189.3	28	−185.6	1394	1.14
Benzene	80.2	394	5.5	126	20	879	1.72
Brine (20% sodium chloride by mass)	103.9	—	−17.4	—	20	1150	3.11
n-Butane	−0.5	385.2	−138.5	80.3	−0.5	601	2.31
Carbon dioxide	−78.4*	230.5 (at 0°C)	−56.6		0	298	0.59
Ethanol	78.2	838.3	−114.2	109	25	783	2.46
Ethyl alcohol	78.6	855	−156	108	20	789	2.84
Ethylene glycol	198.1	800.1	−10.8	181.1	20	1109	2.84
Glycerine	179.9	974	18.9	200.6	20	1261	2.32
Helium	−268.9	22.8	—	—	−268.9	146.2	22.8
Hydrogen	−252.8	445.7	−259.2	59.5	−252.8	70.7	10.0
Isobutane	−11.7	367.1	−160	105.7	−11.7	593.8	2.28
Kerosene	204–293	251	−24.9	—	20	820	2.00
Mercury	356.7	294.7	−38.9	11.4	25	13,560	0.139
Methane	−161.5	510.4	−182.2	58.4	−161.5	423	3.49
					−100	301	5.79
Methanol	64.5	1100	−97.7	99.2	25	787	2.55
Nitrogen	−195.8	198.6	−210	25.3	−195.8	809	2.06
					−160	596	2.97
Octane	124.8	306.3	−57.5	180.7	20	703	2.10
Oil (light)					25	910	1.80
Oxygen	−183	212.7	−218.8	13.7	−183	1141	1.71
Petroleum	—	230–384			20	640	2.0
Propane	−42.1	427.8	−187.7	80.0	−42.1	581	2.25
					0	529	2.53
					50	449	3.13
Refrigerant-134a	−26.1	217.0	−96.6	—	−50	1443	1.23
					−26.1	1374	1.27
					0	1295	1.34
					25	1207	1.43
Water	100	2257	0.0	333.7	0	1000	4.22
					25	997	4.18
					50	988	4.18
					75	975	4.19
					100	958	4.22

* Sublimation temperature. (At pressures below the triple-point pressure of 518 kPa, carbon dioxide exists as a solid or gas. Also, the freezing-point temperature of carbon dioxide is the triple-point temperature of −56.5°C.)

Properties of common liquids, solids, and foods (*Concluded*)

(*b*) Solids (values are for room temperature unless indicated otherwise)

Substance	Density, ρ kg/m^3	Specific heat, c_p kJ/kg · K	Substance	Density, ρ kg/m^3	Specific heat, c_p kJ/kg · K
Metals			Nonmetals		
Aluminum			Asphalt	2110	0.920
200 K		0.797	Brick, common	1922	0.79
250 K		0.859	Brick, fireclay (500°C)	2300	0.960
300 K	2,700	0.902	Concrete	2300	0.653
350 K		0.929	Clay	1000	0.920
400 K		0.949	Diamond	2420	0.616
450 K		0.973	Glass, window	2700	0.800
500 K		0.997	Glass, pyrex	2230	0.840
Bronze (76% Cu, 2% Zn, 2% Al)	8,280	0.400	Graphite	2500	0.711
Brass, yellow (65% Cu, 35% Zn)	8,310	0.400	Granite	2700	1.017
Copper			Gypsum or plaster board	800	1.09
−173°C		0.254	Ice		
−100°C		0.342	200 K		1.56
−50°C		0.367	220 K		1.71
0°C		0.381	240 K		1.86
27°C	8,900	0.386	260 K		2.01
100°C		0.393	273 K	921	2.11
200°C		0.403	Limestone	1650	0.909
Iron	7,840	0.45	Marble	2600	0.880
Lead	11,310	0.128	Plywood (Douglas Fir)	545	1.21
Magnesium	1,730	1.000	Rubber (soft)	1100	1.840
Nickel	8,890	0.440	Rubber (hard)	1150	2.009
Silver	10,470	0.235	Sand	1520	0.800
Steel, mild	7,830	0.500	Stone	1500	0.800
Tungsten	19,400	0.130	Woods, hard (maple, oak, etc.)	721	1.26
			Woods, soft (fir, pine, etc.)	513	1.38

(*c*) Foods

Food	Water content, % (mass)	Freezing point, °C	Specific heat, kJ/kg · K — Above freezing	Specific heat, kJ/kg · K — Below freezing	Latent heat of fusion, kJ/kg	Food	Water content, % (mass)	Freezing point, °C	Specific heat, kJ/kg · K — Above freezing	Specific heat, kJ/kg · K — Below freezing	Latent heat of fusion, kJ/kg
Apples	84	−1.1	3.65	1.90	281	Lettuce	95	−0.2	4.02	2.04	317
Bananas	75	−0.8	3.35	1.78	251	Milk, whole	88	−0.6	3.79	1.95	294
Beef round	67	—	3.08	1.68	224	Oranges	87	−0.8	3.75	1.94	291
Broccoli	90	−0.6	3.86	1.97	301	Potatoes	78	−0.6	3.45	1.82	261
Butter	16	—	—	1.04	53	Salmon fish	64	−2.2	2.98	1.65	214
Cheese, swiss	39	−10.0	2.15	1.33	130	Shrimp	83	−2.2	3.62	1.89	277
Cherries	80	−1.8	3.52	1.85	267	Spinach	93	−0.3	3.96	2.01	311
Chicken	74	−2.8	3.32	1.77	247	Strawberries	90	−0.8	3.86	1.97	301
Corn, sweet	74	−0.6	3.32	1.77	247	Tomatoes, ripe	94	−0.5	3.99	2.02	314
Eggs, whole	74	−0.6	3.32	1.77	247	Turkey	64	—	2.98	1.65	214
Ice cream	63	−5.6	2.95	1.63	210	Watermelon	93	−0.4	3.96	2.01	311

Source: Values are obtained from various handbooks and other sources or are calculated. Water content and freezing-point data of foods are from *ASHRAE, Handbook of Fundamentals,* SI version (Atlanta, GA: American Society of Heating, Refrigerating and Air-Conditioning Engineers, Inc., 1993), Chapter 30, Table 1. Freezing point is the temperature at which freezing starts for fruits and vegetables, and the average freezing temperature for other foods.

TABLE A–4

Saturated water—Temperature table

Temp., T °C	Sat. press., P_{sat} kPa	Specific volume, m³/kg		Internal energy, kJ/kg			Enthalpy, kJ/kg			Entropy, kJ/kg · K		
		Sat. liquid, v_f	Sat. vapor, v_g	Sat. liquid, u_f	Evap., u_{fg}	Sat. vapor, u_g	Sat. liquid, h_f	Evap., h_{fg}	Sat. vapor, h_g	Sat. liquid, s_f	Evap., s_{fg}	Sat. vapor, s_g
0.01	0.6117	0.001000	206.00	0.000	2374.9	2374.9	0.001	2500.9	2500.9	0.0000	9.1556	9.1556
5	0.8725	0.001000	147.03	21.019	2360.8	2381.8	21.020	2489.1	2510.1	0.0763	8.9487	9.0249
10	1.2281	0.001000	106.32	42.020	2346.6	2388.7	42.022	2477.2	2519.2	0.1511	8.7488	8.8999
15	1.7057	0.001001	77.885	62.980	2332.5	2395.5	62.982	2465.4	2528.3	0.2245	8.5559	8.7803
20	2.3392	0.001002	57.762	83.913	2318.4	2402.3	83.915	2453.5	2537.4	0.2965	8.3696	8.6661
25	3.1698	0.001003	43.340	104.83	2304.3	2409.1	104.83	2441.7	2546.5	0.3672	8.1895	8.5567
30	4.2469	0.001004	32.879	125.73	2290.2	2415.9	125.74	2429.8	2555.6	0.4368	8.0152	8.4520
35	5.6291	0.001006	25.205	146.63	2276.0	2422.7	146.64	2417.9	2564.6	0.5051	7.8466	8.3517
40	7.3851	0.001008	19.515	167.53	2261.9	2429.4	167.53	2406.0	2573.5	0.5724	7.6832	8.2556
45	9.5953	0.001010	15.251	188.43	2247.7	2436.1	188.44	2394.0	2582.4	0.6386	7.5247	8.1633
50	12.352	0.001012	12.026	209.33	2233.4	2442.7	209.34	2382.0	2591.3	0.7038	7.3710	8.0748
55	15.763	0.001015	9.5639	230.24	2219.1	2449.3	230.26	2369.8	2600.1	0.7680	7.2218	7.9898
60	19.947	0.001017	7.6670	251.16	2204.7	2455.9	251.18	2357.7	2608.8	0.8313	7.0769	7.9082
65	25.043	0.001020	6.1935	272.09	2190.3	2462.4	272.12	2345.4	2617.5	0.8937	6.9360	7.8296
70	31.202	0.001023	5.0396	293.04	2175.8	2468.9	293.07	2333.0	2626.1	0.9551	6.7989	7.7540
75	38.597	0.001026	4.1291	313.99	2161.3	2475.3	314.03	2320.6	2634.6	1.0158	6.6655	7.6812
80	47.416	0.001029	3.4053	334.97	2146.6	2481.6	335.02	2308.0	2643.0	1.0756	6.5355	7.6111
85	57.868	0.001032	2.8261	355.96	2131.9	2487.8	356.02	2295.3	2651.4	1.1346	6.4089	7.5435
90	70.183	0.001036	2.3593	376.97	2117.0	2494.0	377.04	2282.5	2659.6	1.1929	6.2853	7.4782
95	84.609	0.001040	1.9808	398.00	2102.0	2500.1	398.09	2269.6	2667.6	1.2504	6.1647	7.4151
100	101.42	0.001043	1.6720	419.06	2087.0	2506.0	419.17	2256.4	2675.6	1.3072	6.0470	7.3542
105	120.90	0.001047	1.4186	440.15	2071.8	2511.9	440.28	2243.1	2683.4	1.3634	5.9319	7.2952
110	143.38	0.001052	1.2094	461.27	2056.4	2517.7	461.42	2229.7	2691.1	1.4188	5.8193	7.2382
115	169.18	0.001056	1.0360	482.42	2040.9	2523.3	482.59	2216.0	2698.6	1.4737	5.7092	7.1829
120	198.67	0.001060	0.89133	503.60	2025.3	2528.9	503.81	2202.1	2706.0	1.5279	5.6013	7.1292
125	232.23	0.001065	0.77012	524.83	2009.5	2534.3	525.07	2188.1	2713.1	1.5816	5.4956	7.0771
130	270.28	0.001070	0.66808	546.10	1993.4	2539.5	546.38	2173.7	2720.1	1.6346	5.3919	7.0265
135	313.22	0.001075	0.58179	567.41	1977.3	2544.7	567.75	2159.1	2726.9	1.6872	5.2901	6.9773
140	361.53	0.001080	0.50850	588.77	1960.9	2549.6	589.16	2144.3	2733.5	1.7392	5.1901	6.9294
145	415.68	0.001085	0.44600	610.19	1944.2	2554.4	610.64	2129.2	2739.8	1.7908	5.0919	6.8827
150	476.16	0.001091	0.39248	631.66	1927.4	2559.1	632.18	2113.8	2745.9	1.8418	4.9953	6.8371
155	543.49	0.001096	0.34648	653.19	1910.3	2563.5	653.79	2098.0	2751.8	1.8924	4.9002	6.7927
160	618.23	0.001102	0.30680	674.79	1893.0	2567.8	675.47	2082.0	2757.5	1.9426	4.8066	6.7492
165	700.93	0.001108	0.27244	696.46	1875.4	2571.9	697.24	2065.6	2762.8	1.9923	4.7143	6.7067
170	792.18	0.001114	0.24260	718.20	1857.5	2575.7	719.08	2048.8	2767.9	2.0417	4.6233	6.6650
175	892.60	0.001121	0.21659	740.02	1839.4	2579.4	741.02	2031.7	2772.7	2.0906	4.5335	6.6242
180	1002.8	0.001127	0.19384	761.92	1820.9	2582.8	763.05	2014.2	2777.2	2.1392	4.4448	6.5841
185	1123.5	0.001134	0.17390	783.91	1802.1	2586.0	785.19	1996.2	2781.4	2.1875	4.3572	6.5447
190	1255.2	0.001141	0.15636	806.00	1783.0	2589.0	807.43	1977.9	2785.3	2.2355	4.2705	6.5059
195	1398.8	0.001149	0.14089	828.18	1763.6	2591.7	829.78	1959.0	2788.8	2.2831	4.1847	6.4678
200	1554.9	0.001157	0.12721	850.46	1743.7	2594.2	852.26	1939.8	2792.0	2.3305	4.0997	6.4302

TABLE A–4

Saturated water—Temperature table (Continued)

H₂O

Temp., T °C	Sat. press., P_{sat} kPa	Specific volume, m³/kg		Internal energy, kJ/kg			Enthalpy, kJ/kg			Entropy, kJ/kg · K		
		Sat. liquid, v_f	Sat. vapor, v_g	Sat. liquid, u_f	Evap., u_{fg}	Sat. vapor, u_g	Sat. liquid, h_f	Evap., h_{fg}	Sat. vapor, h_g	Sat. liquid, s_f	Evap., s_{fg}	Sat. vapor, s_g
205	1724.3	0.001164	0.11508	872.86	1723.5	2596.4	874.87	1920.0	2794.8	2.3776	4.0154	6.3930
210	1907.7	0.001173	0.10429	895.38	1702.9	2598.3	897.61	1899.7	2797.3	2.4245	3.9318	6.3563
215	2105.9	0.001181	0.094680	918.02	1681.9	2599.9	920.50	1878.8	2799.3	2.4712	3.8489	6.3200
220	2319.6	0.001190	0.086094	940.79	1660.5	2601.3	943.55	1857.4	2801.0	2.5176	3.7664	6.2840
225	2549.7	0.001199	0.078405	963.70	1638.6	2602.3	966.76	1835.4	2802.2	2.5639	3.6844	6.2483
230	2797.1	0.001209	0.071505	986.76	1616.1	2602.9	990.14	1812.8	2802.9	2.6100	3.6028	6.2128
235	3062.6	0.001219	0.065300	1010.0	1593.2	2603.2	1013.7	1789.5	2803.2	2.6560	3.5216	6.1775
240	3347.0	0.001229	0.059707	1033.4	1569.8	2603.1	1037.5	1765.5	2803.0	2.7018	3.4405	6.1424
245	3651.2	0.001240	0.054656	1056.9	1545.7	2602.7	1061.5	1740.8	2802.2	2.7476	3.3596	6.1072
250	3976.2	0.001252	0.050085	1080.7	1521.1	2601.8	1085.7	1715.3	2801.0	2.7933	3.2788	6.0721
255	4322.9	0.001263	0.045941	1104.7	1495.8	2600.5	1110.1	1689.0	2799.1	2.8390	3.1979	6.0369
260	4692.3	0.001276	0.042175	1128.8	1469.9	2598.7	1134.8	1661.8	2796.6	2.8847	3.1169	6.0017
265	5085.3	0.001289	0.038748	1153.3	1443.2	2596.5	1159.8	1633.7	2793.5	2.9304	3.0358	5.9662
270	5503.0	0.001303	0.035622	1177.9	1415.7	2593.7	1185.1	1604.6	2789.7	2.9762	2.9542	5.9305
275	5946.4	0.001317	0.032767	1202.9	1387.4	2590.3	1210.7	1574.5	2785.2	3.0221	2.8723	5.8944
280	6416.6	0.001333	0.030153	1228.2	1358.2	2586.4	1236.7	1543.2	2779.9	3.0681	2.7898	5.8579
285	6914.6	0.001349	0.027756	1253.7	1328.1	2581.8	1263.1	1510.7	2773.7	3.1144	2.7066	5.8210
290	7441.8	0.001366	0.025554	1279.7	1296.9	2576.5	1289.8	1476.9	2766.7	3.1608	2.6225	5.7834
295	7999.0	0.001384	0.023528	1306.0	1264.5	2570.5	1317.1	1441.6	2758.7	3.2076	2.5374	5.7450
300	8587.9	0.001404	0.021659	1332.7	1230.9	2563.6	1344.8	1404.8	2749.6	3.2548	2.4511	5.7059
305	9209.4	0.001425	0.019932	1360.0	1195.9	2555.8	1373.1	1366.3	2739.4	3.3024	2.3633	5.6657
310	9865.0	0.001447	0.018333	1387.7	1159.3	2547.1	1402.0	1325.9	2727.9	3.3506	2.2737	5.6243
315	10,556	0.001472	0.016849	1416.1	1121.1	2537.2	1431.6	1283.4	2715.0	3.3994	2.1821	5.5816
320	11,284	0.001499	0.015470	1445.1	1080.9	2526.0	1462.0	1238.5	2700.6	3.4491	2.0881	5.5372
325	12,051	0.001528	0.014183	1475.0	1038.5	2513.4	1493.4	1191.0	2684.3	3.4998	1.9911	5.4908
330	12,858	0.001560	0.012979	1505.7	993.5	2499.2	1525.8	1140.3	2666.0	3.5516	1.8906	5.4422
335	13,707	0.001597	0.011848	1537.5	945.5	2483.0	1559.4	1086.0	2645.4	3.6050	1.7857	5.3907
340	14,601	0.001638	0.010783	1570.7	893.8	2464.5	1594.6	1027.4	2622.0	3.6602	1.6756	5.3358
345	15,541	0.001685	0.009772	1605.5	837.7	2443.2	1631.7	963.4	2595.1	3.7179	1.5585	5.2765
350	16,529	0.001741	0.008806	1642.4	775.9	2418.3	1671.2	892.7	2563.9	3.7788	1.4326	5.2114
355	17,570	0.001808	0.007872	1682.2	706.4	2388.6	1714.0	812.9	2526.9	3.8442	1.2942	5.1384
360	18,666	0.001895	0.006950	1726.2	625.7	2351.9	1761.5	720.1	2481.6	3.9165	1.1373	5.0537
365	19,822	0.002015	0.006009	1777.2	526.4	2303.6	1817.2	605.5	2422.7	4.0004	0.9489	4.9493
370	21,044	0.002217	0.004953	1844.5	385.6	2230.1	1891.2	443.1	2334.3	4.1119	0.6890	4.8009
373.95	22,064	0.003106	0.003106	2015.7	0	2015.7	2084.3	0	2084.3	4.4070	0	4.4070

Source: Tables A–4 through A–8 are generated using the Engineering Equation Solver (EES) software developed by S. A. Klein and F. L. Alvarado. The routine used in calculations is the highly accurate Steam_IAPWS, which incorporates the 1995 Formulation for the Thermodynamic Properties of Ordinary Water Substance for General and Scientific Use, issued by The International Association for the Properties of Water and Steam (IAPWS). This formulation replaces the 1984 formulation of Haar, Gallagher, and Kell (NBS/NRC Steam Tables, Hemisphere Publishing Co., 1984), which is also available in EES as the routine STEAM. The new formulation is based on the correlations of Saul and Wagner (J. Phys. Chem. Ref. Data, 16, 893, 1987) with modifications to adjust to the International Temperature Scale of 1990. The modifications are described by Wagner and Pruss (J. Phys. Chem. Ref. Data, 22, 783, 1993). The properties of ice are based on Hyland and Wexler, "Formulations for the Thermodynamic Properties of the Saturated Phases of H₂O from 173.15 K to 473.15 K," *ASHRAE Trans.*, Part 2A, Paper 2793, 1983.

TABLE A–5

Saturated water—Pressure table

Press., P kPa	Sat. temp., T_{sat} °C	Specific volume, m³/kg		Internal energy, kJ/kg			Enthalpy, kJ/kg			Entropy, kJ/kg · K		
		Sat. liquid, v_f	Sat. vapor, v_g	Sat. liquid, u_f	Evap., u_{fg}	Sat. vapor, u_g	Sat. liquid, h_f	Evap., h_{fg}	Sat. vapor, h_g	Sat. liquid, s_f	Evap., s_{fg}	Sat. vapor, s_g
1.0	6.97	0.001000	129.19	29.302	2355.2	2384.5	29.303	2484.4	2513.7	0.1059	8.8690	8.9749
1.5	13.02	0.001001	87.964	54.686	2338.1	2392.8	54.688	2470.1	2524.7	0.1956	8.6314	8.8270
2.0	17.50	0.001001	66.990	73.431	2325.5	2398.9	73.433	2459.5	2532.9	0.2606	8.4621	8.7227
2.5	21.08	0.001002	54.242	88.422	2315.4	2403.8	88.424	2451.0	2539.4	0.3118	8.3302	8.6421
3.0	24.08	0.001003	45.654	100.98	2306.9	2407.9	100.98	2443.9	2544.8	0.3543	8.2222	8.5765
4.0	28.96	0.001004	34.791	121.39	2293.1	2414.5	121.39	2432.3	2553.7	0.4224	8.0510	8.4734
5.0	32.87	0.001005	28.185	137.75	2282.1	2419.8	137.75	2423.0	2560.7	0.4762	7.9176	8.3938
7.5	40.29	0.001008	19.233	168.74	2261.1	2429.8	168.75	2405.3	2574.0	0.5763	7.6738	8.2501
10	45.81	0.001010	14.670	191.79	2245.4	2437.2	191.81	2392.1	2583.9	0.6492	7.4996	8.1488
15	53.97	0.001014	10.020	225.93	2222.1	2448.0	225.94	2372.3	2598.3	0.7549	7.2522	8.0071
20	60.06	0.001017	7.6481	251.40	2204.6	2456.0	251.42	2357.5	2608.9	0.8320	7.0752	7.9073
25	64.96	0.001020	6.2034	271.93	2190.4	2462.4	271.96	2345.5	2617.5	0.8932	6.9370	7.8302
30	69.09	0.001022	5.2287	289.24	2178.5	2467.7	289.27	2335.3	2624.6	0.9441	6.8234	7.7675
40	75.86	0.001026	3.9933	317.58	2158.8	2476.3	317.62	2318.4	2636.1	1.0261	6.6430	7.6691
50	81.32	0.001030	3.2403	340.49	2142.7	2483.2	340.54	2304.7	2645.2	1.0912	6.5019	7.5931
75	91.76	0.001037	2.2172	384.36	2111.8	2496.1	384.44	2278.0	2662.4	1.2132	6.2426	7.4558
100	99.61	0.001043	1.6941	417.40	2088.2	2505.6	417.51	2257.5	2675.0	1.3028	6.0562	7.3589
101.325	99.97	0.001043	1.6734	418.95	2087.0	2506.0	419.06	2256.5	2675.6	1.3069	6.0476	7.3545
125	105.97	0.001048	1.3750	444.23	2068.8	2513.0	444.36	2240.6	2684.9	1.3741	5.9100	7.2841
150	111.35	0.001053	1.1594	466.97	2052.3	2519.2	467.13	2226.0	2693.1	1.4337	5.7894	7.2231
175	116.04	0.001057	1.0037	486.82	2037.7	2524.5	487.01	2213.1	2700.2	1.4850	5.6865	7.1716
200	120.21	0.001061	0.88578	504.50	2024.6	2529.1	504.71	2201.6	2706.3	1.5302	5.5968	7.1270
225	123.97	0.001064	0.79329	520.47	2012.7	2533.2	520.71	2191.0	2711.7	1.5706	5.5171	7.0877
250	127.41	0.001067	0.71873	535.08	2001.8	2536.8	535.35	2181.2	2716.5	1.6072	5.4453	7.0525
275	130.58	0.001070	0.65732	548.57	1991.6	2540.1	548.86	2172.0	2720.9	1.6408	5.3800	7.0207
300	133.52	0.001073	0.60582	561.11	1982.1	2543.2	561.43	2163.5	2724.9	1.6717	5.3200	6.9917
325	136.27	0.001076	0.56199	572.84	1973.1	2545.9	573.19	2155.4	2728.6	1.7005	5.2645	6.9650
350	138.86	0.001079	0.52422	583.89	1964.6	2548.5	584.26	2147.7	2732.0	1.7274	5.2128	6.9402
375	141.30	0.001081	0.49133	594.32	1956.6	2550.9	594.73	2140.4	2735.1	1.7526	5.1645	6.9171
400	143.61	0.001084	0.46242	604.22	1948.9	2553.1	604.66	2133.4	2738.1	1.7765	5.1191	6.8955
450	147.90	0.001088	0.41392	622.65	1934.5	2557.1	623.14	2120.3	2743.4	1.8205	5.0356	6.8561
500	151.83	0.001093	0.37483	639.54	1921.2	2560.7	640.09	2108.0	2748.1	1.8604	4.9603	6.8207
550	155.46	0.001097	0.34261	655.16	1908.8	2563.9	655.77	2096.6	2752.4	1.8970	4.8916	6.7886
600	158.83	0.001101	0.31560	669.72	1897.1	2566.8	670.38	2085.8	2756.2	1.9308	4.8285	6.7593
650	161.98	0.001104	0.29260	683.37	1886.1	2569.4	684.08	2075.5	2759.6	1.9623	4.7699	6.7322
700	164.95	0.001108	0.27278	696.23	1875.6	2571.8	697.00	2065.8	2762.8	1.9918	4.7153	6.7071
750	167.75	0.001111	0.25552	708.40	1865.6	2574.0	709.24	2056.4	2765.7	2.0195	4.6642	6.6837

TABLE A–5

Saturated water—Pressure table (*Continued*)

Press., P kPa	Sat. temp., T_{sat} °C	Specific volume, m³/kg		Internal energy, kJ/kg			Enthalpy, kJ/kg			Entropy, kJ/kg · K		
		Sat. liquid, v_f	Sat. vapor, v_g	Sat. liquid, u_f	Evap., u_{fg}	Sat. vapor, u_g	Sat. liquid, h_f	Evap., h_{fg}	Sat. vapor, h_g	Sat. liquid, s_f	Evap., s_{fg}	Sat. vapor, s_g
800	170.41	0.001115	0.24035	719.97	1856.1	2576.0	720.87	2047.5	2768.3	2.0457	4.6160	6.6616
850	172.94	0.001118	0.22690	731.00	1846.9	2577.9	731.95	2038.8	2770.8	2.0705	4.5705	6.6409
900	175.35	0.001121	0.21489	741.55	1838.1	2579.6	742.56	2030.5	2773.0	2.0941	4.5273	6.6213
950	177.66	0.001124	0.20411	751.67	1829.6	2581.3	752.74	2022.4	2775.2	2.1166	4.4862	6.6027
1000	179.88	0.001127	0.19436	761.39	1821.4	2582.8	762.51	2014.6	2777.1	2.1381	4.4470	6.5850
1100	184.06	0.001133	0.17745	779.78	1805.7	2585.5	781.03	1999.6	2780.7	2.1785	4.3735	6.5520
1200	187.96	0.001138	0.16326	796.96	1790.9	2587.8	798.33	1985.4	2783.8	2.2159	4.3058	6.5217
1300	191.60	0.001144	0.15119	813.10	1776.8	2589.9	814.59	1971.9	2786.5	2.2508	4.2428	6.4936
1400	195.04	0.001149	0.14078	828.35	1763.4	2591.8	829.96	1958.9	2788.9	2.2835	4.1840	6.4675
1500	198.29	0.001154	0.13171	842.82	1750.6	2593.4	844.55	1946.4	2791.0	2.3143	4.1287	6.4430
1750	205.72	0.001166	0.11344	876.12	1720.6	2596.7	878.16	1917.1	2795.2	2.3844	4.0033	6.3877
2000	212.38	0.001177	0.099587	906.12	1693.0	2599.1	908.47	1889.8	2798.3	2.4467	3.8923	6.3390
2250	218.41	0.001187	0.088717	933.54	1667.3	2600.9	936.21	1864.3	2800.5	2.5029	3.7926	6.2954
2500	223.95	0.001197	0.079952	958.87	1643.2	2602.1	961.87	1840.1	2801.9	2.5542	3.7016	6.2558
3000	233.85	0.001217	0.066667	1004.6	1598.5	2603.2	1008.3	1794.9	2803.2	2.6454	3.5402	6.1856
3500	242.56	0.001235	0.057061	1045.4	1557.6	2603.0	1049.7	1753.0	2802.7	2.7253	3.3991	6.1244
4000	250.35	0.001252	0.049779	1082.4	1519.3	2601.7	1087.4	1713.5	2800.8	2.7966	3.2731	6.0696
5000	263.94	0.001286	0.039448	1148.1	1448.9	2597.0	1154.5	1639.7	2794.2	2.9207	3.0530	5.9737
6000	275.59	0.001319	0.032449	1205.8	1384.1	2589.9	1213.8	1570.9	2784.6	3.0275	2.8627	5.8902
7000	285.83	0.001352	0.027378	1258.0	1323.0	2581.0	1267.5	1505.2	2772.6	3.1220	2.6927	5.8148
8000	295.01	0.001384	0.023525	1306.0	1264.5	2570.5	1317.1	1441.6	2758.7	3.2077	2.5373	5.7450
9000	303.35	0.001418	0.020489	1350.9	1207.6	2558.5	1363.7	1379.3	2742.9	3.2866	2.3925	5.6791
10,000	311.00	0.001452	0.018028	1393.3	1151.8	2545.2	1407.8	1317.6	2725.5	3.3603	2.2556	5.6159
11,000	318.08	0.001488	0.015988	1433.9	1096.6	2530.4	1450.2	1256.1	2706.3	3.4299	2.1245	5.5544
12,000	324.68	0.001526	0.014264	1473.0	1041.3	2514.3	1491.3	1194.1	2685.4	3.4964	1.9975	5.4939
13,000	330.85	0.001566	0.012781	1511.0	985.5	2496.6	1531.4	1131.3	2662.7	3.5606	1.8730	5.4336
14,000	336.67	0.001610	0.011487	1548.4	928.7	2477.1	1571.0	1067.0	2637.9	3.6232	1.7497	5.3728
15,000	342.16	0.001657	0.010341	1585.5	870.3	2455.7	1610.3	1000.5	2610.8	3.6848	1.6261	5.3108
16,000	347.36	0.001710	0.009312	1622.6	809.4	2432.0	1649.9	931.1	2581.0	3.7461	1.5005	5.2466
17,000	352.29	0.001770	0.008374	1660.2	745.1	2405.4	1690.3	857.4	2547.7	3.8082	1.3709	5.1791
18,000	356.99	0.001840	0.007504	1699.1	675.9	2375.0	1732.2	777.8	2510.0	3.8720	1.2343	5.1064
19,000	361.47	0.001926	0.006677	1740.3	598.9	2339.2	1776.8	689.2	2466.0	3.9396	1.0860	5.0256
20,000	365.75	0.002038	0.005862	1785.8	509.0	2294.8	1826.6	585.5	2412.1	4.0146	0.9164	4.9310
21,000	369.83	0.002207	0.004994	1841.6	391.9	2233.5	1888.0	450.4	2338.4	4.1071	0.7005	4.8076
22,000	373.71	0.002703	0.003644	1951.7	140.8	2092.4	2011.1	161.5	2172.6	4.2942	0.2496	4.5439
22,064	373.95	0.003106	0.003106	2015.7	0	2015.7	2084.3	0	2084.3	4.4070	0	4.4070

TABLE A–6

Superheated water

T °C	v m³/kg	u kJ/kg	h kJ/kg	s kJ/kg·K	v m³/kg	u kJ/kg	h kJ/kg	s kJ/kg·K	v m³/kg	u kJ/kg	h kJ/kg	s kJ/kg·K
	P = 0.01 MPa (45.81°C)*				P = 0.05 MPa (81.32°C)				P = 0.10 MPa (99.61°C)			
Sat.†	14.670	2437.2	2583.9	8.1488	3.2403	2483.2	2645.2	7.5931	1.6941	2505.6	2675.0	7.3589
50	14.867	2443.3	2592.0	8.1741								
100	17.196	2515.5	2687.5	8.4489	3.4187	2511.5	2682.4	7.6953	1.6959	2506.2	2675.8	7.3611
150	19.513	2587.9	2783.0	8.6893	3.8897	2585.7	2780.2	7.9413	1.9367	2582.9	2776.6	7.6148
200	21.826	2661.4	2879.6	8.9049	4.3562	2660.0	2877.8	8.1592	2.1724	2658.2	2875.5	7.8356
250	24.136	2736.1	2977.5	9.1015	4.8206	2735.1	2976.2	8.3568	2.4062	2733.9	2974.5	8.0346
300	26.446	2812.3	3076.7	9.2827	5.2841	2811.6	3075.8	8.5387	2.6389	2810.7	3074.5	8.2172
400	31.063	2969.3	3280.0	9.6094	6.2094	2968.9	3279.3	8.8659	3.1027	2968.3	3278.6	8.5452
500	35.680	3132.9	3489.7	9.8998	7.1338	3132.6	3489.3	9.1566	3.5655	3132.2	3488.7	8.8362
600	40.296	3303.3	3706.3	10.1631	8.0577	3303.1	3706.0	9.4201	4.0279	3302.8	3705.6	9.0999
700	44.911	3480.8	3929.9	10.4056	8.9813	3480.6	3929.7	9.6626	4.4900	3480.4	3929.4	9.3424
800	49.527	3665.4	4160.6	10.6312	9.9047	3665.2	4160.4	9.8883	4.9519	3665.0	4160.2	9.5682
900	54.143	3856.9	4398.3	10.8429	10.8280	3856.8	4398.2	10.1000	5.4137	3856.7	4398.0	9.7800
1000	58.758	4055.3	4642.8	11.0429	11.7513	4055.2	4642.7	10.3000	5.8755	4055.0	4642.6	9.9800
1100	63.373	4260.0	4893.8	11.2326	12.6745	4259.9	4893.7	10.4897	6.3372	4259.8	4893.6	10.1698
1200	67.989	4470.9	5150.8	11.4132	13.5977	4470.8	5150.7	10.6704	6.7988	4470.7	5150.6	10.3504
1300	72.604	4687.4	5413.4	11.5857	14.5209	4687.3	5413.3	10.8429	7.2605	4687.2	5413.3	10.5229
	P = 0.20 MPa (120.21°C)				P = 0.30 MPa (133.52°C)				P = 0.40 MPa (143.61°C)			
Sat.	0.88578	2529.1	2706.3	7.1270	0.60582	2543.2	2724.9	6.9917	0.46242	2553.1	2738.1	6.8955
150	0.95986	2577.1	2769.1	7.2810	0.63402	2571.0	2761.2	7.0792	0.47088	2564.4	2752.8	6.9306
200	1.08049	2654.6	2870.7	7.5081	0.71643	2651.0	2865.9	7.3132	0.53434	2647.2	2860.9	7.1723
250	1.19890	2731.4	2971.2	7.7100	0.79645	2728.9	2967.9	7.5180	0.59520	2726.4	2964.5	7.3804
300	1.31623	2808.8	3072.1	7.8941	0.87535	2807.0	3069.6	7.7037	0.65489	2805.1	3067.1	7.5677
400	1.54934	2967.2	3277.0	8.2236	1.03155	2966.0	3275.5	8.0347	0.77265	2964.9	3273.9	7.9003
500	1.78142	3131.4	3487.7	8.5153	1.18672	3130.6	3486.6	8.3271	0.88936	3129.8	3485.5	8.1933
600	2.01302	3302.2	3704.8	8.7793	1.34139	3301.6	3704.0	8.5915	1.00558	3301.0	3703.3	8.4580
700	2.24434	3479.9	3928.8	9.0221	1.49580	3479.5	3928.2	8.8345	1.12152	3479.0	3927.6	8.7012
800	2.47550	3664.7	4159.8	9.2479	1.65004	3664.3	4159.3	9.0605	1.23730	3663.9	4158.9	8.9274
900	2.70656	3856.3	4397.7	9.4598	1.80417	3856.0	4397.3	9.2725	1.35298	3855.7	4396.9	9.1394
1000	2.93755	4054.8	4642.3	9.6599	1.95824	4054.5	4642.0	9.4726	1.46859	4054.3	4641.7	9.3396
1100	3.16848	4259.6	4893.3	9.8497	2.11226	4259.4	4893.1	9.6624	1.58414	4259.2	4892.9	9.5295
1200	3.39938	4470.5	5150.4	10.0304	2.26624	4470.3	5150.2	9.8431	1.69966	4470.2	5150.0	9.7102
1300	3.63026	4687.1	5413.1	10.2029	2.42019	4686.9	5413.0	10.0157	1.81516	4686.7	5412.8	9.8828
	P = 0.50 MPa (151.83°C)				P = 0.60 MPa (158.83°C)				P = 0.80 MPa (170.41°C)			
Sat.	0.37483	2560.7	2748.1	6.8207	0.31560	2566.8	2756.2	6.7593	0.24035	2576.0	2768.3	6.6616
200	0.42503	2643.3	2855.8	7.0610	0.35212	2639.4	2850.6	6.9683	0.26088	2631.1	2839.8	6.8177
250	0.47443	2723.8	2961.0	7.2725	0.39390	2721.2	2957.6	7.1833	0.29321	2715.9	2950.4	7.0402
300	0.52261	2803.3	3064.6	7.4614	0.43442	2801.4	3062.0	7.3740	0.32416	2797.5	3056.9	7.2345
350	0.57015	2883.0	3168.1	7.6346	0.47428	2881.6	3166.1	7.5481	0.35442	2878.6	3162.2	7.4107
400	0.61731	2963.7	3272.4	7.7956	0.51374	2962.5	3270.8	7.7097	0.38429	2960.2	3267.7	7.5735
500	0.71095	3129.0	3484.5	8.0893	0.59200	3128.2	3483.4	8.0041	0.44332	3126.6	3481.3	7.8692
600	0.80409	3300.4	3702.5	8.3544	0.66976	3299.8	3701.7	8.2695	0.50186	3298.7	3700.1	8.1354
700	0.89696	3478.6	3927.0	8.5978	0.74725	3478.1	3926.4	8.5132	0.56011	3477.2	3925.3	8.3794
800	0.98966	3663.6	4158.4	8.8240	0.82457	3663.2	4157.9	8.7395	0.61820	3662.5	4157.0	8.6061
900	1.08227	3855.4	4396.6	9.0362	0.90179	3855.1	4396.2	8.9518	0.67619	3854.5	4395.5	8.8185
1000	1.17480	4054.0	4641.4	9.2364	0.97893	4053.8	4641.1	9.1521	0.73411	4053.3	4640.5	9.0189
1100	1.26728	4259.0	4892.6	9.4263	1.05603	4258.8	4892.4	9.3420	0.79197	4258.3	4891.9	9.2090
1200	1.35972	4470.0	5149.8	9.6071	1.13309	4469.8	5149.6	9.5229	0.84980	4469.4	5149.3	9.3898
1300	1.45214	4686.6	5412.6	9.7797	1.21012	4686.4	5412.5	9.6955	0.90761	4686.1	5412.2	9.5625

*The temperature in parentheses is the saturation temperature at the specified pressure.

† Properties of saturated vapor at the specified pressure.

11

TABLE A–6

Superheated water (*Continued*)

T °C	v m³/kg	u kJ/kg	h kJ/kg	s kJ/kg·K	v m³/kg	u kJ/kg	h kJ/kg	s kJ/kg·K	v m³/kg	u kJ/kg	h kJ/kg	s kJ/kg·K
	P = 1.00 MPa (179.88°C)				P = 1.20 MPa (187.96°C)				P = 1.40 MPa (195.04°C)			
Sat.	0.19437	2582.8	2777.1	6.5850	0.16326	2587.8	2783.8	6.5217	0.14078	2591.8	2788.9	6.4675
200	0.20602	2622.3	2828.3	6.6956	0.16934	2612.9	2816.1	6.5909	0.14303	2602.7	2803.0	6.4975
250	0.23275	2710.4	2943.1	6.9265	0.19241	2704.7	2935.6	6.8313	0.16356	2698.9	2927.9	6.7488
300	0.25799	2793.7	3051.6	7.1246	0.21386	2789.7	3046.3	7.0335	0.18233	2785.7	3040.9	6.9553
350	0.28250	2875.7	3158.2	7.3029	0.23455	2872.7	3154.2	7.2139	0.20029	2869.7	3150.1	7.1379
400	0.30661	2957.9	3264.5	7.4670	0.25482	2955.5	3261.3	7.3793	0.21782	2953.1	3258.1	7.3046
500	0.35411	3125.0	3479.1	7.7642	0.29464	3123.4	3477.0	7.6779	0.25216	3121.8	3474.8	7.6047
600	0.40111	3297.5	3698.6	8.0311	0.33395	3296.3	3697.0	7.9456	0.28597	3295.1	3695.5	7.8730
700	0.44783	3476.3	3924.1	8.2755	0.37297	3475.3	3922.9	8.1904	0.31951	3474.4	3921.7	8.1183
800	0.49438	3661.7	4156.1	8.5024	0.41184	3661.0	4155.2	8.4176	0.35288	3660.3	4154.3	8.3458
900	0.54083	3853.9	4394.8	8.7150	0.45059	3853.3	4394.0	8.6303	0.38614	3852.7	4393.3	8.5587
1000	0.58721	4052.7	4640.0	8.9155	0.48928	4052.2	4639.4	8.8310	0.41933	4051.7	4638.8	8.7595
1100	0.63354	4257.9	4891.4	9.1057	0.52792	4257.5	4891.0	9.0212	0.45247	4257.0	4890.5	8.9497
1200	0.67983	4469.0	5148.9	9.2866	0.56652	4468.7	5148.5	9.2022	0.48558	4468.3	5148.1	9.1308
1300	0.72610	4685.8	5411.9	9.4593	0.60509	4685.5	5411.6	9.3750	0.51866	4685.1	5411.3	9.3036
	P = 1.60 MPa (201.37°C)				P = 1.80 MPa (207.11°C)				P = 2.00 MPa (212.38°C)			
Sat.	0.12374	2594.8	2792.8	6.4200	0.11037	2597.3	2795.9	6.3775	0.09959	2599.1	2798.3	6.3390
225	0.13293	2645.1	2857.8	6.5537	0.11678	2637.0	2847.2	6.4825	0.10381	2628.5	2836.1	6.4160
250	0.14190	2692.9	2919.9	6.6753	0.12502	2686.7	2911.7	6.6088	0.11150	2680.3	2903.3	6.5475
300	0.15866	2781.6	3035.4	6.8864	0.14025	2777.4	3029.9	6.8246	0.12551	2773.2	3024.2	6.7684
350	0.17459	2866.6	3146.0	7.0713	0.15460	2863.6	3141.9	7.0120	0.13860	2860.5	3137.7	6.9583
400	0.19007	2950.8	3254.9	7.2394	0.16849	2948.3	3251.6	7.1814	0.15122	2945.9	3248.4	7.1292
500	0.22029	3120.1	3472.6	7.5410	0.19551	3118.5	3470.4	7.4845	0.17568	3116.9	3468.3	7.4337
600	0.24999	3293.9	3693.9	7.8101	0.22200	3292.7	3692.3	7.7543	0.19962	3291.5	3690.7	7.7043
700	0.27941	3473.5	3920.5	8.0558	0.24822	3472.6	3919.4	8.0005	0.22326	3471.7	3918.2	7.9509
800	0.30865	3659.5	4153.4	8.2834	0.27426	3658.8	4152.4	8.2284	0.24674	3658.0	4151.5	8.1791
900	0.33780	3852.1	4392.6	8.4965	0.30020	3851.5	4391.9	8.4417	0.27012	3850.9	4391.1	8.3925
1000	0.36687	4051.2	4638.2	8.6974	0.32606	4050.7	4637.6	8.6427	0.29342	4050.2	4637.1	8.5936
1100	0.39589	4256.6	4890.0	8.8878	0.35188	4256.2	4889.6	8.8331	0.31667	4255.7	4889.1	8.7842
1200	0.42488	4467.9	5147.7	9.0689	0.37766	4467.6	5147.3	9.0143	0.33989	4467.2	5147.0	8.9654
1300	0.45383	4684.8	5410.9	9.2418	0.40341	4684.5	5410.6	9.1872	0.36308	4684.2	5410.3	9.1384
	P = 2.50 MPa (223.95°C)				P = 3.00 MPa (233.85°C)				P = 3.50 MPa (242.56°C)			
Sat.	0.07995	2602.1	2801.9	6.2558	0.06667	2603.2	2803.2	6.1856	0.05706	2603.0	2802.7	6.1244
225	0.08026	2604.8	2805.5	6.2629								
250	0.08705	2663.3	2880.9	6.4107	0.07063	2644.7	2856.5	6.2893	0.05876	2624.0	2829.7	6.1764
300	0.09894	2762.2	3009.6	6.6459	0.08118	2750.8	2994.3	6.5412	0.06845	2738.8	2978.4	6.4484
350	0.10979	2852.5	3127.0	6.8424	0.09056	2844.4	3116.1	6.7450	0.07680	2836.0	3104.9	6.6601
400	0.12012	2939.8	3240.1	7.0170	0.09938	2933.6	3231.7	6.9235	0.08456	2927.2	3223.2	6.8428
450	0.13015	3026.2	3351.6	7.1768	0.10789	3021.2	3344.9	7.0856	0.09198	3016.1	3338.1	7.0074
500	0.13999	3112.8	3462.8	7.3254	0.11620	3108.6	3457.2	7.2359	0.09919	3104.5	3451.7	7.1593
600	0.15931	3288.5	3686.8	7.5979	0.13245	3285.5	3682.8	7.5103	0.11325	3282.5	3678.9	7.4357
700	0.17835	3469.3	3915.2	7.8455	0.14841	3467.0	3912.2	7.7590	0.12702	3464.7	3909.3	7.6855
800	0.19722	3656.2	4149.2	8.0744	0.16420	3654.3	4146.9	7.9885	0.14061	3652.5	4144.6	7.9156
900	0.21597	3849.4	4389.3	8.2882	0.17988	3847.9	4387.5	8.2028	0.15410	3846.4	4385.7	8.1304
1000	0.23466	4049.0	4635.6	8.4897	0.19549	4047.7	4634.2	8.4045	0.16751	4046.4	4632.7	8.3324
1100	0.25330	4254.7	4887.9	8.6804	0.21105	4253.6	4886.7	8.5955	0.18087	4252.5	4885.6	8.5236
1200	0.27190	4466.3	5146.0	8.8618	0.22658	4465.3	5145.1	8.7771	0.19420	4464.4	5144.1	8.7053
1300	0.29048	4683.4	5409.5	9.0349	0.24207	4682.6	5408.8	8.9502	0.20750	4681.8	5408.0	8.8786

TABLE A–6

Superheated water (*Continued*)

T °C	v m³/kg	u kJ/kg	h kJ/kg	s kJ/kg · K	v m³/kg	u kJ/kg	h kJ/kg	s kJ/kg · K	v m³/kg	u kJ/kg	h kJ/kg	s kJ/kg · K
	P = 4.0 MPa (250.35°C)				P = 4.5 MPa (257.44°C)				P = 5.0 MPa (263.94°C)			
Sat.	0.04978	2601.7	2800.8	6.0696	0.04406	2599.7	2798.0	6.0198	0.03945	2597.0	2794.2	5.9737
275	0.05461	2668.9	2887.3	6.2312	0.04733	2651.4	2864.4	6.1429	0.04144	2632.3	2839.5	6.0571
300	0.05887	2726.2	2961.7	6.3639	0.05138	2713.0	2944.2	6.2854	0.04535	2699.0	2925.7	6.2111
350	0.06647	2827.4	3093.3	6.5843	0.05842	2818.6	3081.5	6.5153	0.05197	2809.5	3069.3	6.4516
400	0.07343	2920.8	3214.5	6.7714	0.06477	2914.2	3205.7	6.7071	0.05784	2907.5	3196.7	6.6483
450	0.08004	3011.0	3331.2	6.9386	0.07076	3005.8	3324.2	6.8770	0.06332	3000.6	3317.2	6.8210
500	0.08644	3100.3	3446.0	7.0922	0.07652	3096.0	3440.4	7.0323	0.06858	3091.8	3434.7	6.9781
600	0.09886	3279.4	3674.9	7.3706	0.08766	3276.4	3670.9	7.3127	0.07870	3273.3	3666.9	7.2605
700	0.11098	3462.4	3906.3	7.6214	0.09850	3460.0	3903.3	7.5647	0.08852	3457.7	3900.3	7.5136
800	0.12292	3650.6	4142.3	7.8523	0.10916	3648.8	4140.0	7.7962	0.09816	3646.9	4137.7	7.7458
900	0.13476	3844.8	4383.9	8.0675	0.11972	3843.3	4382.1	8.0118	0.10769	3841.8	4380.2	7.9619
1000	0.14653	4045.1	4631.2	8.2698	0.13020	4043.9	4629.8	8.2144	0.11715	4042.6	4628.3	8.1648
1100	0.15824	4251.4	4884.4	8.4612	0.14064	4250.4	4883.2	8.4060	0.12655	4249.3	4882.1	8.3566
1200	0.16992	4463.5	5143.2	8.6430	0.15103	4462.6	5142.2	8.5880	0.13592	4461.6	5141.3	8.5388
1300	0.18157	4680.9	5407.2	8.8164	0.16140	4680.1	5406.5	8.7616	0.14527	4679.3	5405.7	8.7124
	P = 6.0 MPa (275.59°C)				P = 7.0 MPa (285.83°C)				P = 8.0 MPa (295.01°C)			
Sat.	0.03245	2589.9	2784.6	5.8902	0.027378	2581.0	2772.6	5.8148	0.023525	2570.5	2758.7	5.7450
300	0.03619	2668.4	2885.6	6.0703	0.029492	2633.5	2839.9	5.9337	0.024279	2592.3	2786.5	5.7937
350	0.04225	2790.4	3043.9	6.3357	0.035262	2770.1	3016.9	6.2305	0.029975	2748.3	2988.1	6.1321
400	0.04742	2893.7	3178.3	6.5432	0.039958	2879.5	3159.2	6.4502	0.034344	2864.6	3139.4	6.3658
450	0.05217	2989.9	3302.9	6.7219	0.044187	2979.0	3288.3	6.6353	0.038194	2967.8	3273.3	6.5579
500	0.05667	3083.1	3423.1	6.8826	0.048157	3074.3	3411.4	6.8000	0.041767	3065.4	3399.5	6.7266
550	0.06102	3175.2	3541.3	7.0308	0.051966	3167.9	3531.6	6.9507	0.045172	3160.5	3521.8	6.8800
600	0.06527	3267.2	3658.8	7.1693	0.055665	3261.0	3650.6	7.0910	0.048463	3254.7	3642.4	7.0221
700	0.07355	3453.0	3894.3	7.4247	0.062850	3448.3	3888.3	7.3487	0.054829	3443.6	3882.2	7.2822
800	0.08165	3643.2	4133.1	7.6582	0.069856	3639.5	4128.5	7.5836	0.061011	3635.7	4123.8	7.5185
900	0.08964	3838.8	4376.6	7.8751	0.076750	3835.7	4373.0	7.8014	0.067082	3832.7	4369.3	7.7372
1000	0.09756	4040.1	4625.4	8.0786	0.083571	4037.5	4622.5	8.0055	0.073079	4035.0	4619.6	7.9419
1100	0.10543	4247.1	4879.7	8.2709	0.090341	4245.0	4877.4	8.1982	0.079025	4242.8	4875.0	8.1350
1200	0.11326	4459.8	5139.4	8.4534	0.097075	4457.9	5137.4	8.3810	0.084934	4456.1	5135.5	8.3181
1300	0.12107	4677.7	5404.1	8.6273	0.103781	4676.1	5402.6	8.5551	0.090817	4674.5	5401.0	8.4925
	P = 9.0 MPa (303.35°C)				P = 10.0 MPa (311.00°C)				P = 12.5 MPa (327.81°C)			
Sat.	0.020489	2558.5	2742.9	5.6791	0.018028	2545.2	2725.5	5.6159	0.013496	2505.6	2674.3	5.4638
325	0.023284	2647.6	2857.1	5.8738	0.019877	2611.6	2810.3	5.7596				
350	0.025816	2725.0	2957.3	6.0380	0.022440	2699.6	2924.0	5.9460	0.016138	2624.9	2826.6	5.7130
400	0.029960	2849.2	3118.8	6.2876	0.026436	2833.1	3097.5	6.2141	0.020030	2789.6	3040.0	6.0433
450	0.033524	2956.3	3258.0	6.4872	0.029782	2944.5	3242.4	6.4219	0.023019	2913.7	3201.5	6.2749
500	0.036793	3056.3	3387.4	6.6603	0.032811	3047.0	3375.1	6.5995	0.025630	3023.2	3343.6	6.4651
550	0.039885	3153.0	3512.0	6.8164	0.035655	3145.4	3502.0	6.7585	0.028033	3126.1	3476.5	6.6317
600	0.042861	3248.4	3634.1	6.9605	0.038378	3242.0	3625.8	6.9045	0.030306	3225.8	3604.6	6.7828
650	0.045755	3343.4	3755.2	7.0954	0.041018	3338.0	3748.1	7.0408	0.032491	3324.1	3730.2	6.9227
700	0.048589	3438.8	3876.1	7.2229	0.043597	3434.0	3870.0	7.1693	0.034612	3422.0	3854.6	7.0540
800	0.054132	3632.0	4119.2	7.4606	0.048629	3628.2	4114.5	7.4085	0.038724	3618.8	4102.8	7.2967
900	0.059562	3829.6	4365.7	7.6802	0.053547	3826.5	4362.0	7.6290	0.042720	3818.9	4352.9	7.5195
1000	0.064919	4032.4	4616.7	7.8855	0.058391	4029.9	4613.8	7.8349	0.046641	4023.5	4606.5	7.7269
1100	0.070224	4240.7	4872.7	8.0791	0.063183	4238.5	4870.3	8.0289	0.050510	4233.1	4864.5	7.9220
1200	0.075492	4454.2	5133.6	8.2625	0.067938	4452.4	5131.7	8.2126	0.054342	4447.7	5127.0	8.1065
1300	0.080733	4672.9	5399.5	8.4371	0.072667	4671.3	5398.0	8.3874	0.058147	4667.3	5394.1	8.2819

H₂O

13

TABLE A–6

Superheated water (*Concluded*)

T °C	v m³/kg	u kJ/kg	h kJ/kg	s kJ/kg·K	v m³/kg	u kJ/kg	h kJ/kg	s kJ/kg·K	v m³/kg	u kJ/kg	h kJ/kg	s kJ/kg·K
	P = 15.0 MPa (342.16°C)				*P* = 17.5 MPa (354.67°C)				*P* = 20.0 MPa (365.75°C)			
Sat.	0.010341	2455.7	2610.8	5.3108	0.007932	2390.7	2529.5	5.1435	0.005862	2294.8	2412.1	4.9310
350	0.011481	2520.9	2693.1	5.4438								
400	0.015671	2740.6	2975.7	5.8819	0.012463	2684.3	2902.4	5.7211	0.009950	2617.9	2816.9	5.5526
450	0.018477	2880.8	3157.9	6.1434	0.015204	2845.4	3111.4	6.0212	0.012721	2807.3	3061.7	5.9043
500	0.020828	2998.4	3310.8	6.3480	0.017385	2972.4	3276.7	6.2424	0.014793	2945.3	3241.2	6.1446
550	0.022945	3106.2	3450.4	6.5230	0.019305	3085.8	3423.6	6.4266	0.016571	3064.7	3396.2	6.3390
600	0.024921	3209.3	3583.1	6.6796	0.021073	3192.5	3561.3	6.5890	0.018185	3175.3	3539.0	6.5075
650	0.026804	3310.1	3712.1	6.8233	0.022742	3295.8	3693.8	6.7366	0.019695	3281.4	3675.3	6.6593
700	0.028621	3409.8	3839.1	6.9573	0.024342	3397.5	3823.5	6.8735	0.021134	3385.1	3807.8	6.7991
800	0.032121	3609.3	4091.1	7.2037	0.027405	3599.7	4079.3	7.1237	0.023870	3590.1	4067.5	7.0531
900	0.035503	3811.2	4343.7	7.4288	0.030348	3803.5	4334.6	7.3511	0.026484	3795.7	4325.4	7.2829
1000	0.038808	4017.1	4599.2	7.6378	0.033215	4010.7	4592.0	7.5616	0.029020	4004.3	4584.7	7.4950
1100	0.042062	4227.7	4858.6	7.8339	0.036029	4222.3	4852.8	7.7588	0.031504	4216.9	4847.0	7.6933
1200	0.045279	4443.1	5122.3	8.0192	0.038806	4438.5	5117.6	7.9449	0.033952	4433.8	5112.9	7.8802
1300	0.048469	4663.3	5390.3	8.1952	0.041556	4659.2	5386.5	8.1215	0.036371	4655.2	5382.7	8.0574
	P = 25.0 MPa				*P* = 30.0 MPa				*P* = 35.0 MPa			
375	0.001978	1799.9	1849.4	4.0345	0.001792	1738.1	1791.9	3.9313	0.001701	1702.8	1762.4	3.8724
400	0.006005	2428.5	2578.7	5.1400	0.002798	2068.9	2152.8	4.4758	0.002105	1914.9	1988.6	4.2144
425	0.007886	2607.8	2805.0	5.4708	0.005299	2452.9	2611.8	5.1473	0.003434	2253.3	2373.5	4.7751
450	0.009176	2721.2	2950.6	5.6759	0.006737	2618.9	2821.0	5.4422	0.004957	2497.5	2671.0	5.1946
500	0.011143	2887.3	3165.9	5.9643	0.008691	2824.0	3084.8	5.7956	0.006933	2755.3	2997.9	5.6331
550	0.012736	3020.8	3339.2	6.1816	0.010175	2974.5	3279.7	6.0403	0.008348	2925.8	3218.0	5.9093
600	0.014140	3140.0	3493.5	6.3637	0.011445	3103.4	3446.8	6.2373	0.009523	3065.6	3399.0	6.1229
650	0.015430	3251.9	3637.7	6.5243	0.012590	3221.7	3599.4	6.4074	0.010565	3190.9	3560.7	6.3030
700	0.016643	3359.9	3776.0	6.6702	0.013654	3334.3	3743.9	6.5599	0.011523	3308.3	3711.6	6.4623
800	0.018922	3570.7	4043.8	6.9322	0.015628	3551.2	4020.0	6.8301	0.013278	3531.6	3996.3	6.7409
900	0.021075	3780.2	4307.1	7.1668	0.017473	3764.6	4288.8	7.0695	0.014904	3749.0	4270.6	6.9853
1000	0.023150	3991.5	4570.2	7.3821	0.019240	3978.6	4555.8	7.2880	0.016450	3965.8	4541.5	7.2069
1100	0.025172	4206.1	4835.4	7.5825	0.020954	4195.2	4823.9	7.4906	0.017942	4184.4	4812.4	7.4118
1200	0.027157	4424.6	5103.5	7.7710	0.022630	4415.3	5094.2	7.6807	0.019398	4406.1	5085.0	7.6034
1300	0.029115	4647.2	5375.1	7.9494	0.024279	4639.2	5367.6	7.8602	0.020827	4631.2	5360.2	7.7841
	P = 40.0 MPa				*P* = 50.0 MPa				*P* = 60.0 MPa			
375	0.001641	1677.0	1742.6	3.8290	0.001560	1638.6	1716.6	3.7642	0.001503	1609.7	1699.9	3.7149
400	0.001911	1855.0	1931.4	4.1145	0.001731	1787.8	1874.4	4.0029	0.001633	1745.2	1843.2	3.9317
425	0.002538	2097.5	2199.0	4.5044	0.002009	1960.3	2060.7	4.2746	0.001816	1892.9	2001.8	4.1630
450	0.003692	2364.2	2511.8	4.9449	0.002487	2160.3	2284.7	4.5896	0.002086	2055.1	2180.2	4.4140
500	0.005623	2681.6	2906.5	5.4744	0.003890	2528.1	2722.6	5.1762	0.002952	2393.2	2570.3	4.9356
550	0.006985	2875.1	3154.4	5.7857	0.005118	2769.5	3025.4	5.5563	0.003955	2664.6	2901.9	5.3517
600	0.008089	3026.8	3350.4	6.0170	0.006108	2947.1	3252.6	5.8245	0.004833	2866.8	3156.8	5.6527
650	0.009053	3159.5	3521.6	6.2078	0.006957	3095.6	3443.5	6.0373	0.005591	3031.3	3366.8	5.8867
700	0.009930	3282.0	3679.2	6.3740	0.007717	3228.7	3614.6	6.2179	0.006265	3175.4	3551.3	6.0814
800	0.011521	3511.8	3972.6	6.6613	0.009073	3472.2	3925.8	6.5225	0.007456	3432.6	3880.0	6.4033
900	0.012980	3733.3	4252.5	6.9107	0.010296	3702.0	4216.8	6.7819	0.008519	3670.9	4182.1	6.6725
1000	0.014360	3952.9	4527.3	7.1355	0.011441	3927.4	4499.4	7.0131	0.009504	3902.0	4472.2	6.9099
1100	0.015686	4173.7	4801.1	7.3425	0.012534	4152.2	4778.9	7.2244	0.010439	4130.9	4757.3	7.1255
1200	0.016976	4396.9	5075.9	7.5357	0.013590	4378.6	5058.1	7.4207	0.011339	4360.5	5040.8	7.3248
1300	0.018239	4623.3	5352.8	7.7175	0.014620	4607.5	5338.5	7.6048	0.012213	4591.8	5324.5	7.5111

H₂O

TABLE A–7

Compressed liquid water

T °C	v m³/kg	u kJ/kg	h kJ/kg	s kJ/kg · K	v m³/kg	u kJ/kg	h kJ/kg	s kJ/kg · K	v m³/kg	u kJ/kg	h kJ/kg	s kJ/kg · K
		$P = 5$ MPa (263.94°C)				$P = 10$ MPa (311.00°C)				$P = 15$ MPa (342.16°C)		
Sat.	0.0012862	1148.1	1154.5	2.9207	0.0014522	1393.3	1407.9	3.3603	0.0016572	1585.5	1610.3	3.6848
0	0.0009977	0.04	5.03	0.0001	0.0009952	0.12	10.07	0.0003	0.0009928	0.18	15.07	0.0004
20	0.0009996	83.61	88.61	0.2954	0.0009973	83.31	93.28	0.2943	0.0009951	83.01	97.93	0.2932
40	0.0010057	166.92	171.95	0.5705	0.0010035	166.33	176.37	0.5685	0.0010013	165.75	180.77	0.5666
60	0.0010149	250.29	255.36	0.8287	0.0010127	249.43	259.55	0.8260	0.0010105	248.58	263.74	0.8234
80	0.0010267	333.82	338.96	1.0723	0.0010244	332.69	342.94	1.0691	0.0010221	331.59	346.92	1.0659
100	0.0010410	417.65	422.85	1.3034	0.0010385	416.23	426.62	1.2996	0.0010361	414.85	430.39	1.2958
120	0.0010576	501.91	507.19	1.5236	0.0010549	500.18	510.73	1.5191	0.0010522	498.50	514.28	1.5148
140	0.0010769	586.80	592.18	1.7344	0.0010738	584.72	595.45	1.7293	0.0010708	582.69	598.75	1.7243
160	0.0010988	672.55	678.04	1.9374	0.0010954	670.06	681.01	1.9316	0.0010920	667.63	684.01	1.9259
180	0.0011240	759.47	765.09	2.1338	0.0011200	756.48	767.68	2.1271	0.0011160	753.58	770.32	2.1206
200	0.0011531	847.92	853.68	2.3251	0.0011482	844.32	855.80	2.3174	0.0011435	840.84	858.00	2.3100
220	0.0011868	938.39	944.32	2.5127	0.0011809	934.01	945.82	2.5037	0.0011752	929.81	947.43	2.4951
240	0.0012268	1031.6	1037.7	2.6983	0.0012192	1026.2	1038.3	2.6876	0.0012121	1021.0	1039.2	2.6774
260	0.0012755	1128.5	1134.9	2.8841	0.0012653	1121.6	1134.3	2.8710	0.0012560	1115.1	1134.0	2.8586
280					0.0013226	1221.8	1235.0	3.0565	0.0013096	1213.4	1233.0	3.0410
300					0.0013980	1329.4	1343.3	3.2488	0.0013783	1317.6	1338.3	3.2279
320									0.0014733	1431.9	1454.0	3.4263
340									0.0016311	1567.9	1592.4	3.6555
		$P = 20$ MPa (365.75°C)				$P = 30$ MPa				$P = 50$ MPa		
Sat.	0.0020378	1785.8	1826.6	4.0146								
0	0.0009904	0.23	20.03	0.0005	0.0009857	0.29	29.86	0.0003	0.0009767	0.29	49.13	−0.0010
20	0.0009929	82.71	102.57	0.2921	0.0009886	82.11	111.77	0.2897	0.0009805	80.93	129.95	0.2845
40	0.0009992	165.17	185.16	0.5646	0.0009951	164.05	193.90	0.5607	0.0009872	161.90	211.25	0.5528
60	0.0010084	247.75	267.92	0.8208	0.0010042	246.14	276.26	0.8156	0.0009962	243.08	292.88	0.8055
80	0.0010199	330.50	350.90	1.0627	0.0010155	328.40	358.86	1.0564	0.0010072	324.42	374.78	1.0442
100	0.0010337	413.50	434.17	1.2920	0.0010290	410.87	441.74	1.2847	0.0010201	405.94	456.94	1.2705
120	0.0010496	496.85	517.84	1.5105	0.0010445	493.66	525.00	1.5020	0.0010349	487.69	539.43	1.4859
140	0.0010679	580.71	602.07	1.7194	0.0010623	576.90	608.76	1.7098	0.0010517	569.77	622.36	1.6916
160	0.0010886	665.28	687.05	1.9203	0.0010823	660.74	693.21	1.9094	0.0010704	652.33	705.85	1.8889
180	0.0011122	750.78	773.02	2.1143	0.0011049	745.40	778.55	2.1020	0.0010914	735.49	790.06	2.0790
200	0.0011390	837.49	860.27	2.3027	0.0011304	831.11	865.02	2.2888	0.0011149	819.45	875.19	2.2628
220	0.0011697	925.77	949.16	2.4867	0.0011595	918.15	952.93	2.4707	0.0011412	904.39	961.45	2.4414
240	0.0012053	1016.1	1040.2	2.6676	0.0011927	1006.9	1042.7	2.6491	0.0011708	990.55	1049.1	2.6156
260	0.0012472	1109.0	1134.0	2.8469	0.0012314	1097.8	1134.7	2.8250	0.0012044	1078.2	1138.4	2.7864
280	0.0012978	1205.6	1231.5	3.0265	0.0012770	1191.5	1229.8	3.0001	0.0012430	1167.7	1229.9	2.9547
300	0.0013611	1307.2	1334.4	3.2091	0.0013322	1288.9	1328.9	3.1761	0.0012879	1259.6	1324.0	3.1218
320	0.0014450	1416.6	1445.5	3.3996	0.0014014	1391.7	1433.7	3.3558	0.0013409	1354.3	1421.4	3.2888
340	0.0015693	1540.2	1571.6	3.6086	0.0014932	1502.4	1547.1	3.5438	0.0014049	1452.9	1523.1	3.4575
360	0.0018248	1703.6	1740.1	3.8787	0.0016276	1626.8	1675.6	3.7499	0.0014848	1556.5	1630.7	3.6301
380					0.0018729	1782.0	1838.2	4.0026	0.0015884	1667.1	1746.5	3.8102

Saturated ice–water vapor

Temp., T °C	Sat. press., P_{sat} kPa	Specific volume, m³/kg		Internal energy, kJ/kg			Enthalpy, kJ/kg			Entropy, kJ/kg · K		
		Sat. ice, v_i	Sat. vapor, v_g	Sat. ice, u_i	Subl., u_{ig}	Sat. vapor, u_g	Sat. ice, h_i	Subl., h_{ig}	Sat. vapor, h_g	Sat. ice, s_i	Subl., s_{ig}	Sat. vapor, s_g
0.01	0.61169	0.001091	205.99	−333.40	2707.9	2374.5	−333.40	2833.9	2500.5	−1.2202	10.374	9.154
0	0.61115	0.001091	206.17	−333.43	2707.9	2374.5	−333.43	2833.9	2500.5	−1.2204	10.375	9.154
−2	0.51772	0.001091	241.62	−337.63	2709.4	2371.8	−337.63	2834.5	2496.8	−1.2358	10.453	9.218
−4	0.43748	0.001090	283.84	−341.80	2710.8	2369.0	−341.80	2835.0	2493.2	−1.2513	10.533	9.282
−6	0.36873	0.001090	334.27	−345.94	2712.2	2366.2	−345.93	2835.4	2489.5	−1.2667	10.613	9.347
−8	0.30998	0.001090	394.66	−350.04	2713.5	2363.5	−350.04	2835.8	2485.8	−1.2821	10.695	9.413
−10	0.25990	0.001089	467.17	−354.12	2714.8	2360.7	−354.12	2836.2	2482.1	−1.2976	10.778	9.480
−12	0.21732	0.001089	554.47	−358.17	2716.1	2357.9	−358.17	2836.6	2478.4	−1.3130	10.862	9.549
−14	0.18121	0.001088	659.88	−362.18	2717.3	2355.2	−362.18	2836.9	2474.7	−1.3284	10.947	9.618
−16	0.15068	0.001088	787.51	−366.17	2718.6	2352.4	−366.17	2837.2	2471.0	−1.3439	11.033	9.689
−18	0.12492	0.001088	942.51	−370.13	2719.7	2349.6	−370.13	2837.5	2467.3	−1.3593	11.121	9.761
−20	0.10326	0.001087	1131.3	−374.06	2720.9	2346.8	−374.06	2837.7	2463.6	−1.3748	11.209	9.835
−22	0.08510	0.001087	1362.0	−377.95	2722.0	2344.1	−377.95	2837.9	2459.9	−1.3903	11.300	9.909
−24	0.06991	0.001087	1644.7	−381.82	2723.1	2341.3	−381.82	2838.1	2456.2	−1.4057	11.391	9.985
−26	0.05725	0.001087	1992.2	−385.66	2724.2	2338.5	−385.66	2838.2	2452.5	−1.4212	11.484	10.063
−28	0.04673	0.001086	2421.0	−389.47	2725.2	2335.7	−389.47	2838.3	2448.8	−1.4367	11.578	10.141
−30	0.03802	0.001086	2951.7	−393.25	2726.2	2332.9	−393.25	2838.4	2445.1	−1.4521	11.673	10.221
−32	0.03082	0.001086	3610.9	−397.00	2727.2	2330.2	−397.00	2838.4	2441.4	−1.4676	11.770	10.303
−34	0.02490	0.001085	4432.4	−400.72	2728.1	2327.4	−400.72	2838.5	2437.7	−1.4831	11.869	10.386
−36	0.02004	0.001085	5460.1	−404.40	2729.0	2324.6	−404.40	2838.4	2434.0	−1.4986	11.969	10.470
−38	0.01608	0.001085	6750.5	−408.07	2729.9	2321.8	−408.07	2838.4	2430.3	−1.5141	12.071	10.557
−40	0.01285	0.001084	8376.7	−411.70	2730.7	2319.0	−411.70	2838.3	2426.6	−1.5296	12.174	10.644

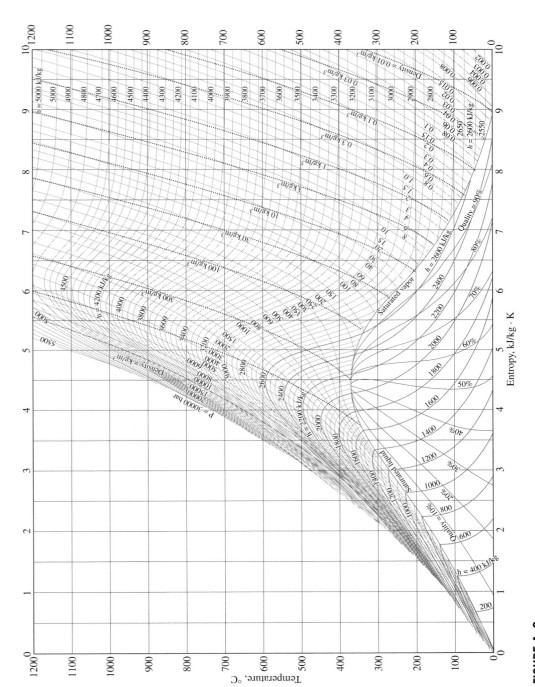

FIGURE A–9

T-s diagram for water.

Copyright © 1984. From NBS/NRC Steam Tables/1 by Lester Haar, John S. Gallagher, and George S. Kell. Reproduced by permission of Routledge/Taylor & Francis Books, Inc.

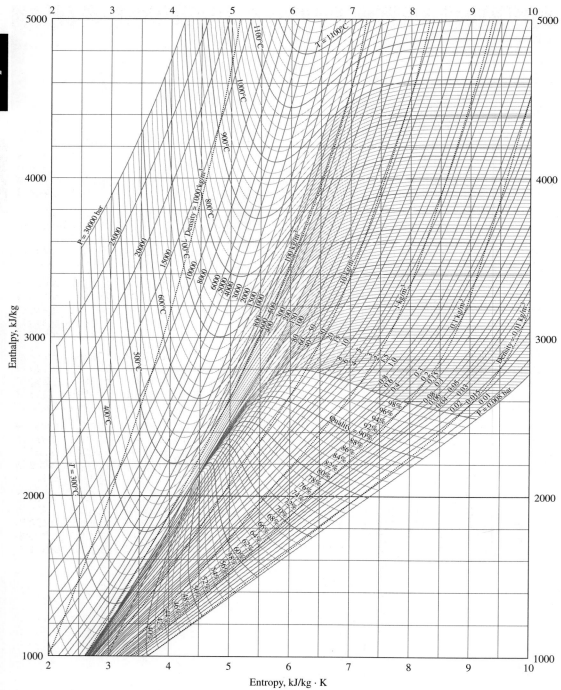

FIGURE A-10

Mollier diagram for water.

Copyright © 1984. From NBS/NRC Steam Tables/1 *by Lester Haar, John S. Gallagher, and George S. Kell. Reproduced by permission of Routledge/Taylor & Francis Books, Inc.*

TABLE A–11

Saturated refrigerant-134a—Temperature table

Temp., T °C	Sat. press., P_{sat} kPa	Specific volume, m³/kg		Internal energy, kJ/kg			Enthalpy, kJ/kg			Entropy, kJ/kg · K		
		Sat. liquid, v_f	Sat. vapor, v_g	Sat. liquid, u_f	Evap., u_{fg}	Sat. vapor, u_g	Sat. liquid, h_f	Evap., h_{fg}	Sat. vapor, h_g	Sat. liquid, s_f	Evap., s_{fg}	Sat. vapor, s_g
−40	51.25	0.0007054	0.36081	−0.036	207.40	207.37	0.000	225.86	225.86	0.00000	0.96866	0.96866
−38	56.86	0.0007083	0.32732	2.475	206.04	208.51	2.515	224.61	227.12	0.01072	0.95511	0.96584
−36	62.95	0.0007112	0.29751	4.992	204.67	209.66	5.037	223.35	228.39	0.02138	0.94176	0.96315
−34	69.56	0.0007142	0.27090	7.517	203.29	210.81	7.566	222.09	229.65	0.03199	0.92859	0.96058
−32	76.71	0.0007172	0.24711	10.05	201.91	211.96	10.10	220.81	230.91	0.04253	0.91560	0.95813
−30	84.43	0.0007203	0.22580	12.59	200.52	213.11	12.65	219.52	232.17	0.05301	0.90278	0.95579
−28	92.76	0.0007234	0.20666	15.13	199.12	214.25	15.20	218.22	233.43	0.06344	0.89012	0.95356
−26	101.73	0.0007265	0.18946	17.69	197.72	215.40	17.76	216.92	234.68	0.07382	0.87762	0.95144
−24	111.37	0.0007297	0.17395	20.25	196.30	216.55	20.33	215.59	235.92	0.08414	0.86527	0.94941
−22	121.72	0.0007329	0.15995	22.82	194.88	217.70	22.91	214.26	s237.17	0.09441	0.85307	0.94748
−20	132.82	0.0007362	0.14729	25.39	193.45	218.84	25.49	212.91	238.41	0.10463	0.84101	0.94564
−18	144.69	0.0007396	0.13583	27.98	192.01	219.98	28.09	211.55	239.64	0.11481	0.82908	0.94389
−16	157.38	0.0007430	0.12542	30.57	190.56	221.13	30.69	210.18	240.87	0.12493	0.81729	0.94222
−14	170.93	0.0007464	0.11597	33.17	189.09	222.27	33.30	208.79	242.09	0.13501	0.80561	0.94063
−12	185.37	0.0007499	0.10736	35.78	187.62	223.40	35.92	207.38	243.30	0.14504	0.79406	0.93911
−10	200.74	0.0007535	0.099516	38.40	186.14	224.54	38.55	205.96	244.51	0.15504	0.78263	0.93766
−8	217.08	0.0007571	0.092352	41.03	184.64	225.67	41.19	204.52	245.72	0.16498	0.77130	0.93629
−6	234.44	0.0007608	0.085802	43.66	183.13	226.80	43.84	203.07	246.91	0.17489	0.76008	0.93497
−4	252.85	0.0007646	0.079804	46.31	181.61	227.92	46.50	201.60	248.10	0.18476	0.74896	0.93372
−2	272.36	0.0007684	0.074304	48.96	180.08	229.04	49.17	200.11	249.28	0.19459	0.73794	0.93253
0	293.01	0.0007723	0.069255	51.63	178.53	230.16	51.86	198.60	250.45	0.20439	0.72701	0.93139
2	314.84	0.0007763	0.064612	54.30	176.97	231.27	54.55	197.07	251.61	0.21415	0.71616	0.93031
4	337.90	0.0007804	0.060338	56.99	175.39	232.38	57.25	195.51	252.77	0.22387	0.70540	0.92927
6	362.23	0.0007845	0.056398	59.68	173.80	233.48	59.97	193.94	253.91	0.23356	0.69471	0.92828
8	387.88	0.0007887	0.052762	62.39	172.19	234.58	62.69	192.35	255.04	0.24323	0.68410	0.92733
10	414.89	0.0007930	0.049403	65.10	170.56	235.67	65.43	190.73	256.16	0.25286	0.67356	0.92641
12	443.31	0.0007975	0.046295	67.83	168.92	236.75	68.18	189.09	257.27	0.26246	0.66308	0.92554
14	473.19	0.0008020	0.043417	70.57	167.26	237.83	70.95	187.42	258.37	0.27204	0.65266	0.92470
16	504.58	0.0008066	0.040748	73.32	165.58	238.90	73.73	185.73	259.46	0.28159	0.64230	0.92389
18	537.52	0.0008113	0.038271	76.08	163.88	239.96	76.52	184.01	260.53	0.29112	0.63198	0.92310

Saturated refrigerant-134a—Temperature table (*Continued*)

R-134a

		Specific volume, m³/kg		Internal energy, kJ/kg			Enthalpy, kJ/kg			Entropy, kJ/kg · K		
Temp., $T\,°C$	Sat. press., P_{sat} kPa	Sat. liquid, v_f	Sat. vapor, v_g	Sat. liquid, u_f	Evap., u_{fg}	Sat. vapor, u_g	Sat. liquid, h_f	Evap., h_{fg}	Sat. vapor, h_g	Sat. liquid, s_f	Evap., s_{fg}	Sat. vapor, s_g
20	572.07	0.0008161	0.035969	78.86	162.16	241.02	79.32	182.27	261.59	0.30063	0.62172	0.92234
22	608.27	0.0008210	0.033828	81.64	160.42	242.06	82.14	180.49	262.64	0.31011	0.61149	0.92160
24	646.18	0.0008261	0.031834	84.44	158.65	243.10	84.98	178.69	263.67	0.31958	0.60130	0.92088
26	685.84	0.0008313	0.029976	87.26	156.87	244.12	87.83	176.85	264.68	0.32903	0.59115	0.92018
28	727.31	0.0008366	0.028242	90.09	155.05	245.14	90.69	174.99	265.68	0.33846	0.58102	0.91948
30	770.64	0.0008421	0.026622	92.93	153.22	246.14	93.58	173.08	266.66	0.34789	0.57091	0.91879
32	815.89	0.0008478	0.025108	95.79	151.35	247.14	96.48	171.14	267.62	0.35730	0.56082	0.91811
34	863.11	0.0008536	0.023691	98.66	149.46	248.12	99.40	169.17	268.57	0.36670	0.55074	0.91743
36	912.35	0.0008595	0.022364	101.55	147.54	249.08	102.33	167.16	269.49	0.37609	0.54066	0.91675
38	963.68	0.0008657	0.021119	104.45	145.58	250.04	105.29	165.10	270.39	0.38548	0.53058	0.91606
40	1017.1	0.0008720	0.019952	107.38	143.60	250.97	108.26	163.00	271.27	0.39486	0.52049	0.91536
42	1072.8	0.0008786	0.018855	110.32	141.58	251.89	111.26	160.86	272.12	0.40425	0.51039	0.91464
44	1130.7	0.0008854	0.017824	113.28	139.52	252.80	114.28	158.67	272.95	0.41363	0.50027	0.91391
46	1191.0	0.0008924	0.016853	116.26	137.42	253.68	117.32	156.43	273.75	0.42302	0.49012	0.91315
48	1253.6	0.0008996	0.015939	119.26	135.29	254.55	120.39	154.14	274.53	0.43242	0.47993	0.91236
52	1386.2	0.0009150	0.014265	125.33	130.88	256.21	126.59	149.39	275.98	0.45126	0.45941	0.91067
56	1529.1	0.0009317	0.012771	131.49	126.28	257.77	132.91	144.38	277.30	0.47018	0.43863	0.90880
60	1682.8	0.0009498	0.011434	137.76	121.46	259.22	139.36	139.10	278.46	0.48920	0.41749	0.90669
65	1891.0	0.0009750	0.009950	145.77	115.05	260.82	147.62	132.02	279.64	0.51320	0.39039	0.90359
70	2118.2	0.0010037	0.008642	154.01	108.14	262.15	156.13	124.32	280.46	0.53755	0.36227	0.89982
75	2365.8	0.0010372	0.007480	162.53	100.60	263.13	164.98	115.85	280.82	0.56241	0.33272	0.89512
80	2635.3	0.0010772	0.006436	171.40	92.23	263.63	174.24	106.35	280.59	0.58800	0.30111	0.88912
85	2928.2	0.0011270	0.005486	180.77	82.67	263.44	184.07	95.44	279.51	0.61473	0.26644	0.88117
90	3246.9	0.0011933	0.004599	190.89	71.29	262.18	194.76	82.35	277.11	0.64336	0.22674	0.87010
95	3594.1	0.0012933	0.003726	202.40	56.47	258.87	207.05	65.21	272.26	0.67578	0.17711	0.85289
100	3975.1	0.0015269	0.002630	218.72	29.19	247.91	224.79	33.58	258.37	0.72217	0.08999	0.81215

Source: Tables A–11 through A–13 are generated using the Engineering Equation Solver (EES) software developed by S. A. Klein and F. L. Alvarado. The routine used in calculations is the R134a, which is based on the fundamental equation of state developed by R. Tillner-Roth and H.D. Baehr, "An International Standard Formulation for the Thermodynamic Properties of 1,1,1,2-Tetrafluoroethane (HFC-134a) for temperatures from 170 K to 455 K and Pressures up to 70 MPa," *J. Phys. Chem, Ref. Data*, Vol. 23, No. 5, 1994. The enthalpy and entropy values of saturated liquid are set to zero at −40°C (and −40°F).

Saturated refrigerant-134a—Pressure table

Press., P kPa	Sat. temp., T_{sat} °C	Specific volume, m³/kg		Internal energy, kJ/kg			Enthalpy, kJ/kg			Entropy, kJ/kg · K		
		Sat. liquid, v_f	Sat. vapor, v_g	Sat. liquid, u_f	Evap., u_{fg}	Sat. vapor, u_g	Sat. liquid, h_f	Evap., h_{fg}	Sat. vapor, h_g	Sat. liquid, s_f	Evap., s_{fg}	Sat. vapor, s_g
60	−36.95	0.0007098	0.31121	3.798	205.32	209.12	3.841	223.95	227.79	0.01634	0.94807	0.96441
70	−33.87	0.0007144	0.26929	7.680	203.20	210.88	7.730	222.00	229.73	0.03267	0.92775	0.96042
80	−31.13	0.0007185	0.23753	11.15	201.30	212.46	11.21	220.25	231.46	0.04711	0.90999	0.95710
90	−28.65	0.0007223	0.21263	14.31	199.57	213.88	14.37	218.65	233.02	0.06008	0.89419	0.95427
100	−26.37	0.0007259	0.19254	17.21	197.98	215.19	17.28	217.16	234.44	0.07188	0.87995	0.95183
120	−22.32	0.0007324	0.16212	22.40	195.11	217.51	22.49	214.48	236.97	0.09275	0.85503	0.94779
140	−18.77	0.0007383	0.14014	26.98	192.57	219.54	27.08	212.08	239.16	0.11087	0.83368	0.94456
160	−15.60	0.0007437	0.12348	31.09	190.27	221.35	31.21	209.90	241.11	0.12693	0.81496	0.94190
180	−12.73	0.0007487	0.11041	34.83	188.16	222.99	34.97	207.90	242.86	0.14139	0.79826	0.93965
200	−10.09	0.0007533	0.099867	38.28	186.21	224.48	38.43	206.03	244.46	0.15457	0.78316	0.93773
240	−5.38	0.0007620	0.083897	44.48	182.67	227.14	44.66	202.62	247.28	0.17794	0.75664	0.93458
280	−1.25	0.0007699	0.072352	49.97	179.50	229.46	50.18	199.54	249.72	0.19829	0.73381	0.93210
320	2.46	0.0007772	0.063604	54.92	176.61	231.52	55.16	196.71	251.88	0.21637	0.71369	0.93006
360	5.82	0.0007841	0.056738	59.44	173.94	233.38	59.72	194.08	253.81	0.23270	0.69566	0.92836
400	8.91	0.0007907	0.051201	63.62	171.45	235.07	63.94	191.62	255.55	0.24761	0.67929	0.92691
450	12.46	0.0007985	0.045619	68.45	168.54	237.00	68.81	188.71	257.53	0.26465	0.66069	0.92535
500	15.71	0.0008059	0.041118	72.93	165.82	238.75	73.33	185.98	259.30	0.28023	0.64377	0.92400
550	18.73	0.0008130	0.037408	77.10	163.25	240.35	77.54	183.38	260.92	0.29461	0.62821	0.92282
600	21.55	0.0008199	0.034295	81.02	160.81	241.83	81.51	180.90	262.40	0.30799	0.61378	0.92177
650	24.20	0.0008266	0.031646	84.72	158.48	243.20	85.26	178.51	263.77	0.32051	0.60030	0.92081
700	26.69	0.0008331	0.029361	88.24	156.24	244.48	88.82	176.21	265.03	0.33230	0.58763	0.91994
750	29.06	0.0008395	0.027371	91.59	154.08	245.67	92.22	173.98	266.20	0.34345	0.57567	0.91912
800	31.31	0.0008458	0.025621	94.79	152.00	246.79	95.47	171.82	267.29	0.35404	0.56431	0.91835
850	33.45	0.0008520	0.024069	97.87	149.98	247.85	98.60	169.71	268.31	0.36413	0.55349	0.91762
900	35.51	0.0008580	0.022683	100.83	148.01	248.85	101.61	167.66	269.26	0.37377	0.54315	0.91692
950	37.48	0.0008641	0.021438	103.69	146.10	249.79	104.51	165.64	270.15	0.38301	0.53323	0.91624
1000	39.37	0.0008700	0.020313	106.45	144.23	250.68	107.32	163.67	270.99	0.39189	0.52368	0.91558
1200	46.29	0.0008934	0.016715	116.70	137.11	253.81	117.77	156.10	273.87	0.42441	0.48863	0.91303
1400	52.40	0.0009166	0.014107	125.94	130.43	256.37	127.22	148.90	276.12	0.45315	0.45734	0.91050
1600	57.88	0.0009400	0.012123	134.43	124.04	258.47	135.93	141.93	277.86	0.47911	0.42873	0.90784
1800	62.87	0.0009639	0.010559	142.33	117.83	260.17	144.07	135.11	279.17	0.50294	0.40204	0.90498
2000	67.45	0.0009886	0.009288	149.78	111.73	261.51	151.76	128.33	280.09	0.52509	0.37675	0.90184
2500	77.54	0.0010566	0.006936	166.99	96.47	263.45	169.63	111.16	280.79	0.57531	0.31695	0.89226
3000	86.16	0.0011406	0.005275	183.04	80.22	263.26	186.46	92.63	279.09	0.62118	0.25776	0.87894

R-134a

TABLE A–13

Superheated refrigerant-134a

T °C	v m³/kg	u kJ/kg	h kJ/kg	s kJ/kg · K	v m³/kg	u kJ/kg	h kJ/kg	s kJ/kg · K	v m³/kg	u kJ/kg	h kJ/kg	s kJ/kg · K
	$P = 0.06$ MPa ($T_{sat} = -36.95°C$)				$P = 0.10$ MPa ($T_{sat} = -26.37°C$)				$P = 0.14$ MPa ($T_{sat} = -18.77°C$)			
Sat.	0.31121	209.12	227.79	0.9644	0.19254	215.19	234.44	0.9518	0.14014	219.54	239.16	0.9446
−20	0.33608	220.60	240.76	1.0174	0.19841	219.66	239.50	0.9721				
−10	0.35048	227.55	248.58	1.0477	0.20743	226.75	247.49	1.0030	0.14605	225.91	246.36	0.9724
0	0.36476	234.66	256.54	1.0774	0.21630	233.95	255.58	1.0332	0.15263	233.23	254.60	1.0031
10	0.37893	241.92	264.66	1.1066	0.22506	241.30	263.81	1.0628	0.15908	240.66	262.93	1.0331
20	0.39302	249.35	272.94	1.1353	0.23373	248.79	272.17	1.0918	0.16544	248.22	271.38	1.0624
30	0.40705	256.95	281.37	1.1636	0.24233	256.44	280.68	1.1203	0.17172	255.93	279.97	1.0912
40	0.42102	264.71	289.97	1.1915	0.25088	264.25	289.34	1.1484	0.17794	263.79	288.70	1.1195
50	0.43495	272.64	298.74	1.2191	0.25937	272.22	298.16	1.1762	0.18412	271.79	297.57	1.1474
60	0.44883	280.73	307.66	1.2463	0.26783	280.35	307.13	1.2035	0.19025	279.96	306.59	1.1749
70	0.46269	288.99	316.75	1.2732	0.27626	288.64	316.26	1.2305	0.19635	288.28	315.77	1.2020
80	0.47651	297.41	326.00	1.2997	0.28465	297.08	325.55	1.2572	0.20242	296.75	325.09	1.2288
90	0.49032	306.00	335.42	1.3260	0.29303	305.69	334.99	1.2836	0.20847	305.38	334.57	1.2553
100	0.50410	314.74	344.99	1.3520	0.30138	314.46	344.60	1.3096	0.21449	314.17	344.20	1.2814
	$P = 0.18$ MPa ($T_{sat} = -12.73°C$)				$P = 0.20$ MPa ($T_{sat} = -10.09°C$)				$P = 0.24$ MPa ($T_{sat} = -5.38°C$)			
Sat.	0.11041	222.99	242.86	0.9397	0.09987	224.48	244.46	0.9377	0.08390	227.14	247.28	0.9346
−10	0.11189	225.02	245.16	0.9484	0.09991	224.55	244.54	0.9380				
0	0.11722	232.48	253.58	0.9798	0.10481	232.09	253.05	0.9698	0.08617	231.29	251.97	0.9519
10	0.12240	240.00	262.04	1.0102	0.10955	239.67	261.58	1.0004	0.09026	238.98	260.65	0.9831
20	0.12748	247.64	270.59	1.0399	0.11418	247.35	270.18	1.0303	0.09423	246.74	269.36	1.0134
30	0.13248	255.41	279.25	1.0690	0.11874	255.14	278.89	1.0595	0.09812	254.61	278.16	1.0429
40	0.13741	263.31	288.05	1.0975	0.12322	263.08	287.72	1.0882	0.10193	262.59	287.06	1.0718
50	0.14230	271.36	296.98	1.1256	0.12766	271.15	296.68	1.1163	0.10570	270.71	296.08	1.1001
60	0.14715	279.56	306.05	1.1532	0.13206	279.37	305.78	1.1441	0.10942	278.97	305.23	1.1280
70	0.15196	287.91	315.27	1.1805	0.13641	287.73	315.01	1.1714	0.11310	287.36	314.51	1.1554
80	0.15673	296.42	324.63	1.2074	0.14074	296.25	324.40	1.1983	0.11675	295.91	323.93	1.1825
90	0.16149	305.07	334.14	1.2339	0.14504	304.92	333.93	1.2249	0.12038	304.60	333.49	1.2092
100	0.16622	313.88	343.80	1.2602	0.14933	313.74	343.60	1.2512	0.12398	313.44	343.20	1.2356
	$P = 0.28$ MPa ($T_{sat} = -1.25°C$)				$P = 0.32$ MPa ($T_{sat} = 2.46°C$)				$P = 0.40$ MPa ($T_{sat} = 8.91°C$)			
Sat.	0.07235	229.46	249.72	0.9321	0.06360	231.52	251.88	0.9301	0.051201	235.07	255.55	0.9269
0	0.07282	230.44	250.83	0.9362								
10	0.07646	238.27	259.68	0.9680	0.06609	237.54	258.69	0.9544	0.051506	235.97	256.58	0.9305
20	0.07997	246.13	268.52	0.9987	0.06925	245.50	267.66	0.9856	0.054213	244.18	265.86	0.9628
30	0.08338	254.06	277.41	1.0285	0.07231	253.50	276.65	1.0157	0.056796	252.36	275.07	0.9937
40	0.08672	262.10	286.38	1.0576	0.07530	261.60	285.70	1.0451	0.059292	260.58	284.30	1.0236
50	0.09000	270.27	295.47	1.0862	0.07823	269.82	294.85	1.0739	0.061724	268.90	293.59	1.0528
60	0.09324	278.56	304.67	1.1142	0.08111	278.15	304.11	1.1021	0.064104	277.32	302.96	1.0814
70	0.09644	286.99	314.00	1.1418	0.08395	286.62	313.48	1.1298	0.066443	285.86	312.44	1.1094
80	0.09961	295.57	323.46	1.1690	0.08675	295.22	322.98	1.1571	0.068747	294.53	322.02	1.1369
90	0.10275	304.29	333.06	1.1958	0.08953	303.97	332.62	1.1840	0.071023	303.32	331.73	1.1640
100	0.10587	313.15	342.80	1.2222	0.09229	312.86	342.39	1.2105	0.073274	312.26	341.57	1.1907
110	0.10897	322.16	352.68	1.2483	0.09503	321.89	352.30	1.2367	0.075504	321.33	351.53	1.2171
120	0.11205	331.32	362.70	1.2742	0.09775	331.07	362.35	1.2626	0.077717	330.55	361.63	1.2431
130	0.11512	340.63	372.87	1.2997	0.10045	340.39	372.54	1.2882	0.079913	339.90	371.87	1.2688
140	0.11818	350.09	383.18	1.3250	0.10314	349.86	382.87	1.3135	0.082096	349.41	382.24	1.2942

R-134a

Superheated refrigerant-134a (*Continued*)

T °C	v m³/kg	u kJ/kg	h kJ/kg	s kJ/kg · K	v m³/kg	u kJ/kg	h kJ/kg	s kJ/kg · K	v m³/kg	u kJ/kg	h kJ/kg	s kJ/kg · K
	$P = 0.50$ MPa ($T_{sat} = 15.71$°C)				$P = 0.60$ MPa ($T_{sat} = 21.55$°C)				$P = 0.70$ MPa ($T_{sat} = 26.69$°C)			
Sat.	0.041118	238.75	259.30	0.9240	0.034295	241.83	262.40	0.9218	0.029361	244.48	265.03	0.9199
20	0.042115	242.40	263.46	0.9383								
30	0.044338	250.84	273.01	0.9703	0.035984	249.22	270.81	0.9499	0.029966	247.48	268.45	0.9313
40	0.046456	259.26	282.48	1.0011	0.037865	257.86	280.58	0.9816	0.031696	256.39	278.57	0.9641
50	0.048499	267.72	291.96	1.0309	0.039659	266.48	290.28	1.0121	0.033322	265.20	288.53	0.9954
60	0.050485	276.25	301.50	1.0599	0.041389	275.15	299.98	1.0417	0.034875	274.01	298.42	1.0256
70	0.052427	284.89	311.10	1.0883	0.043069	283.89	309.73	1.0705	0.036373	282.87	308.33	1.0549
80	0.054331	293.64	320.80	1.1162	0.044710	292.73	319.55	1.0987	0.037829	291.80	318.28	1.0835
90	0.056205	302.51	330.61	1.1436	0.046318	301.67	329.46	1.1264	0.039250	300.82	328.29	1.1114
100	0.058053	311.50	340.53	1.1705	0.047900	310.73	339.47	1.1536	0.040642	309.95	338.40	1.1389
110	0.059880	320.63	350.57	1.1971	0.049458	319.91	349.59	1.1803	0.042010	319.19	348.60	1.1658
120	0.061687	329.89	360.73	1.2233	0.050997	329.23	359.82	1.2067	0.043358	328.55	358.90	1.1924
130	0.063479	339.29	371.03	1.2491	0.052519	338.67	370.18	1.2327	0.044688	338.04	369.32	1.2186
140	0.065256	348.83	381.46	1.2747	0.054027	348.25	380.66	1.2584	0.046004	347.66	379.86	1.2444
150	0.067021	358.51	392.02	1.2999	0.055522	357.96	391.27	1.2838	0.047306	357.41	390.52	1.2699
160	0.068775	368.33	402.72	1.3249	0.057006	367.81	402.01	1.3088	0.048597	367.29	401.31	1.2951
	$P = 0.80$ MPa ($T_{sat} = 31.31$°C)				$P = 0.90$ MPa ($T_{sat} = 35.51$°C)				$P = 1.00$ MPa ($T_{sat} = 39.37$°C)			
Sat.	0.025621	246.79	267.29	0.9183	0.022683	248.85	269.26	0.9169	0.020313	250.68	270.99	0.9156
40	0.027035	254.82	276.45	0.9480	0.023375	253.13	274.17	0.9327	0.020406	251.30	271.71	0.9179
50	0.028547	263.86	286.69	0.9802	0.024809	262.44	284.77	0.9660	0.021796	260.94	282.74	0.9525
60	0.029973	272.83	296.81	1.0110	0.026146	271.60	295.13	0.9976	0.023068	270.32	293.38	0.9850
70	0.031340	281.81	306.88	1.0408	0.027413	280.72	305.39	1.0280	0.024261	279.59	303.85	1.0160
80	0.032659	290.84	316.97	1.0698	0.028630	289.86	315.63	1.0574	0.025398	288.86	314.25	1.0458
90	0.033941	299.95	327.10	1.0981	0.029806	299.06	325.89	1.0860	0.026492	298.15	324.64	1.0748
100	0.035193	309.15	337.30	1.1258	0.030951	308.34	336.19	1.1140	0.027552	307.51	335.06	1.1031
110	0.036420	318.45	347.59	1.1530	0.032068	317.70	346.56	1.1414	0.028584	316.94	345.53	1.1308
120	0.037625	327.87	357.97	1.1798	0.033164	327.18	357.02	1.1684	0.029592	326.47	356.06	1.1580
130	0.038813	337.40	368.45	1.2061	0.034241	336.76	367.58	1.1949	0.030581	336.11	366.69	1.1846
140	0.039985	347.06	379.05	1.2321	0.035302	346.46	378.23	1.2210	0.031554	345.85	377.40	1.2109
150	0.041143	356.85	389.76	1.2577	0.036349	356.28	389.00	1.2467	0.032512	355.71	388.22	1.2368
160	0.042290	366.76	400.59	1.2830	0.037384	366.23	399.88	1.2721	0.033457	365.70	399.15	1.2623
170	0.043427	376.81	411.55	1.3080	0.038408	376.31	410.88	1.2972	0.034392	375.81	410.20	1.2875
180	0.044554	386.99	422.64	1.3327	0.039423	386.52	422.00	1.3221	0.035317	386.04	421.36	1.3124
	$P = 1.20$ MPa ($T_{sat} = 46.29$°C)				$P = 1.40$ MPa ($T_{sat} = 52.40$°C)				$P = 1.60$ MPa ($T_{sat} = 57.88$°C)			
Sat.	0.016715	253.81	273.87	0.9130	0.014107	256.37	276.12	0.9105	0.012123	258.47	277.86	0.9078
50	0.017201	257.63	278.27	0.9267								
60	0.018404	267.56	289.64	0.9614	0.015005	264.46	285.47	0.9389	0.012372	260.89	280.69	0.9163
70	0.019502	277.21	300.61	0.9938	0.016060	274.62	297.10	0.9733	0.013430	271.76	293.25	0.9535
80	0.020529	286.75	311.39	1.0248	0.017023	284.51	308.34	1.0056	0.014362	282.09	305.07	0.9875
90	0.021506	296.26	322.07	1.0546	0.017923	294.28	319.37	1.0364	0.015215	292.17	316.52	1.0194
100	0.022442	305.80	332.73	1.0836	0.018778	304.01	330.30	1.0661	0.016014	302.14	327.76	1.0500
110	0.023348	315.38	343.40	1.1118	0.019597	313.76	341.19	1.0949	0.016773	312.07	338.91	1.0795
120	0.024228	325.03	354.11	1.1394	0.020388	323.55	352.09	1.1230	0.017500	322.02	350.02	1.1081
130	0.025086	334.77	364.88	1.1664	0.021155	333.41	363.02	1.1504	0.018201	332.00	361.12	1.1360
140	0.025927	344.61	375.72	1.1930	0.021904	343.34	374.01	1.1773	0.018882	342.05	372.26	1.1632
150	0.026753	354.56	386.66	1.2192	0.022636	353.37	385.07	1.2038	0.019545	352.17	383.44	1.1900
160	0.027566	364.61	397.69	1.2449	0.023355	363.51	396.20	1.2298	0.020194	362.38	394.69	1.2163
170	0.028367	374.78	408.82	1.2703	0.024061	373.75	407.43	1.2554	0.020830	372.69	406.02	1.2421
180	0.029158	385.08	420.07	1.2954	0.024757	384.10	418.76	1.2807	0.021456	383.11	417.44	1.2676

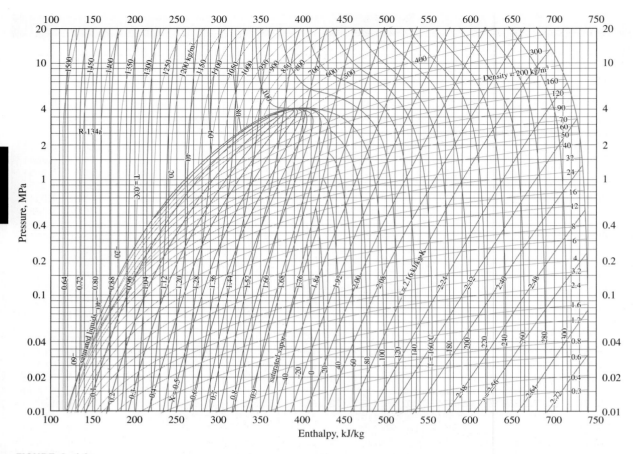

FIGURE A–14

P-h diagram for refrigerant-134a.

Note: The reference point used for the chart is different than that used in the R-134a tables. Therefore, problems should be solved using all property data either from the tables or from the chart, but not from both.

Reprinted by permission of American Society of Heating, Refrigerating, and Air-Conditioning Engineers, Inc., Atlanta, GA.

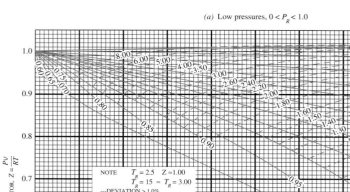

(a) Low pressures, $0 < P_R < 1.0$

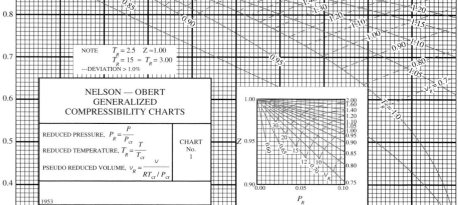

NOTE $T_R = 2.5$ $Z \approx 1.00$
$T_R = 15 \approx T_R = 3.00$
---DEVIATION > 1.0%

NELSON — OBERT
GENERALIZED
COMPRESSIBILITY CHARTS

REDUCED PRESSURE, $P_R = \dfrac{P}{P_{cr}}$

REDUCED TEMPERATURE, $T_R = \dfrac{T}{T_{cr}}$

PSEUDO REDUCED VOLUME, $v_R = \dfrac{v}{RT_{cr}/P_{cr}}$

CHART No. 1

1953

(b) Intermediate pressures, $0 < P_R < 7$

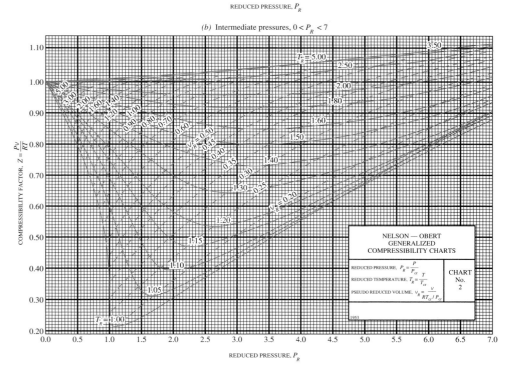

NELSON — OBERT
GENERALIZED
COMPRESSIBILITY CHARTS

REDUCED PRESSURE, $P_R = \dfrac{P}{P_{cr}}$

REDUCED TEMPERATURE, $T_R = \dfrac{T}{T_{cr}}$

PSEUDO REDUCED VOLUME, $v_R = \dfrac{v}{RT_{cr}/P_{cr}}$

CHART No. 2

1953

FIGURE A–15

Nelson–Obert generalized compressibility chart.

Used with permission of Dr. Edward E. Obert, University of Wisconsin.

TABLE A–16

Properties of the atmosphere at high altitude

Altitude, m	Temperature, °C	Pressure, kPa	Gravity g, m/s²	Speed of Sound, m/s	Density, kg/m³	Viscosity μ, kg/m · s	Thermal Conductivity, W/m · K
0	15.00	101.33	9.807	340.3	1.225	1.789×10^{-5}	0.0253
200	13.70	98.95	9.806	339.5	1.202	1.783×10^{-5}	0.0252
400	12.40	96.61	9.805	338.8	1.179	1.777×10^{-5}	0.0252
600	11.10	94.32	9.805	338.0	1.156	1.771×10^{-5}	0.0251
800	9.80	92.08	9.804	337.2	1.134	1.764×10^{-5}	0.0250
1000	8.50	89.88	9.804	336.4	1.112	1.758×10^{-5}	0.0249
1200	7.20	87.72	9.803	335.7	1.090	1.752×10^{-5}	0.0248
1400	5.90	85.60	9.802	334.9	1.069	1.745×10^{-5}	0.0247
1600	4.60	83.53	9.802	334.1	1.048	1.739×10^{-5}	0.0245
1800	3.30	81.49	9.801	333.3	1.027	1.732×10^{-5}	0.0244
2000	2.00	79.50	9.800	332.5	1.007	1.726×10^{-5}	0.0243
2200	0.70	77.55	9.800	331.7	0.987	1.720×10^{-5}	0.0242
2400	−0.59	75.63	9.799	331.0	0.967	1.713×10^{-5}	0.0241
2600	−1.89	73.76	9.799	330.2	0.947	1.707×10^{-5}	0.0240
2800	−3.19	71.92	9.798	329.4	0.928	1.700×10^{-5}	0.0239
3000	−4.49	70.12	9.797	328.6	0.909	1.694×10^{-5}	0.0238
3200	−5.79	68.36	9.797	327.8	0.891	1.687×10^{-5}	0.0237
3400	−7.09	66.63	9.796	327.0	0.872	1.681×10^{-5}	0.0236
3600	−8.39	64.94	9.796	326.2	0.854	1.674×10^{-5}	0.0235
3800	−9.69	63.28	9.795	325.4	0.837	1.668×10^{-5}	0.0234
4000	−10.98	61.66	9.794	324.6	0.819	1.661×10^{-5}	0.0233
4200	−12.3	60.07	9.794	323.8	0.802	1.655×10^{-5}	0.0232
4400	−13.6	58.52	9.793	323.0	0.785	1.648×10^{-5}	0.0231
4600	−14.9	57.00	9.793	322.2	0.769	1.642×10^{-5}	0.0230
4800	−16.2	55.51	9.792	321.4	0.752	1.635×10^{-5}	0.0229
5000	−17.5	54.05	9.791	320.5	0.736	1.628×10^{-5}	0.0228
5200	−18.8	52.62	9.791	319.7	0.721	1.622×10^{-5}	0.0227
5400	−20.1	51.23	9.790	318.9	0.705	1.615×10^{-5}	0.0226
5600	−21.4	49.86	9.789	318.1	0.690	1.608×10^{-5}	0.0224
5800	−22.7	48.52	9.785	317.3	0.675	1.602×10^{-5}	0.0223
6000	−24.0	47.22	9.788	316.5	0.660	1.595×10^{-5}	0.0222
6200	−25.3	45.94	9.788	315.6	0.646	1.588×10^{-5}	0.0221
6400	−26.6	44.69	9.787	314.8	0.631	1.582×10^{-5}	0.0220
6600	−27.9	43.47	9.786	314.0	0.617	1.575×10^{-5}	0.0219
6800	−29.2	42.27	9.785	313.1	0.604	1.568×10^{-5}	0.0218
7000	−30.5	41.11	9.785	312.3	0.590	1.561×10^{-5}	0.0217
8000	−36.9	35.65	9.782	308.1	0.526	1.527×10^{-5}	0.0212
9000	−43.4	30.80	9.779	303.8	0.467	1.493×10^{-5}	0.0206
10,000	−49.9	26.50	9.776	299.5	0.414	1.458×10^{-5}	0.0201
12,000	−56.5	19.40	9.770	295.1	0.312	1.422×10^{-5}	0.0195
14,000	−56.5	14.17	9.764	295.1	0.228	1.422×10^{-5}	0.0195
16,000	−56.5	10.53	9.758	295.1	0.166	1.422×10^{-5}	0.0195
18,000	−56.5	7.57	9.751	295.1	0.122	1.422×10^{-5}	0.0195

Source: U.S. Standard Atmosphere Supplements, U.S. Government Printing Office, 1966. Based on year-round mean conditions at 45° latitude and varies with the time of the year and the weather patterns. The conditions at sea level ($z = 0$) are taken to be $P = 101.325$ kPa, $T = 15$°C, $\rho = 1.2250$ kg/m³, $g = 9.80665$ m²/s.

TABLE A–17

Ideal-gas properties of air

T K	h kJ/kg	P_r	u kJ/kg	v_r	$s°$ kJ/kg · K	T K	h kJ/kg	P_r	u kJ/kg	v_r	$s°$ kJ/kg · K
200	199.97	0.3363	142.56	1707.0	1.29559	580	586.04	14.38	419.55	115.7	2.37348
210	209.97	0.3987	149.69	1512.0	1.34444	590	596.52	15.31	427.15	110.6	2.39140
220	219.97	0.4690	156.82	1346.0	1.39105	600	607.02	16.28	434.78	105.8	2.40902
230	230.02	0.5477	164.00	1205.0	1.43557	610	617.53	17.30	442.42	101.2	2.42644
240	240.02	0.6355	171.13	1084.0	1.47824	620	628.07	18.36	450.09	96.92	2.44356
250	250.05	0.7329	178.28	979.0	1.51917	630	638.63	19.84	457.78	92.84	2.46048
260	260.09	0.8405	185.45	887.8	1.55848	640	649.22	20.64	465.50	88.99	2.47716
270	270.11	0.9590	192.60	808.0	1.59634	650	659.84	21.86	473.25	85.34	2.49364
280	280.13	1.0889	199.75	738.0	1.63279	660	670.47	23.13	481.01	81.89	2.50985
285	285.14	1.1584	203.33	706.1	1.65055	670	681.14	24.46	488.81	78.61	2.52589
290	290.16	1.2311	206.91	676.1	1.66802	680	691.82	25.85	496.62	75.50	2.54175
295	295.17	1.3068	210.49	647.9	1.68515	690	702.52	27.29	504.45	72.56	2.55731
298	298.18	1.3543	212.64	631.9	1.69528	700	713.27	28.80	512.33	69.76	2.57277
300	300.19	1.3860	214.07	621.2	1.70203	710	724.04	30.38	520.23	67.07	2.58810
305	305.22	1.4686	217.67	596.0	1.71865	720	734.82	32.02	528.14	64.53	2.60319
310	310.24	1.5546	221.25	572.3	1.73498	730	745.62	33.72	536.07	62.13	2.61803
315	315.27	1.6442	224.85	549.8	1.75106	740	756.44	35.50	544.02	59.82	2.63280
320	320.29	1.7375	228.42	528.6	1.76690	750	767.29	37.35	551.99	57.63	2.64737
325	325.31	1.8345	232.02	508.4	1.78249	760	778.18	39.27	560.01	55.54	2.66176
330	330.34	1.9352	235.61	489.4	1.79783	780	800.03	43.35	576.12	51.64	2.69013
340	340.42	2.149	242.82	454.1	1.82790	800	821.95	47.75	592.30	48.08	2.71787
350	350.49	2.379	250.02	422.2	1.85708	820	843.98	52.59	608.59	44.84	2.74504
360	360.58	2.626	257.24	393.4	1.88543	840	866.08	57.60	624.95	41.85	2.77170
370	370.67	2.892	264.46	367.2	1.91313	860	888.27	63.09	641.40	39.12	2.79783
380	380.77	3.176	271.69	343.4	1.94001	880	910.56	68.98	657.95	36.61	2.82344
390	390.88	3.481	278.93	321.5	1.96633	900	932.93	75.29	674.58	34.31	2.84856
400	400.98	3.806	286.16	301.6	1.99194	920	955.38	82.05	691.28	32.18	2.87324
410	411.12	4.153	293.43	283.3	2.01699	940	977.92	89.28	708.08	30.22	2.89748
420	421.26	4.522	300.69	266.6	2.04142	960	1000.55	97.00	725.02	28.40	2.92128
430	431.43	4.915	307.99	251.1	2.06533	980	1023.25	105.2	741.98	26.73	2.94468
440	441.61	5.332	315.30	236.8	2.08870	1000	1046.04	114.0	758.94	25.17	2.96770
450	451.80	5.775	322.62	223.6	2.11161	1020	1068.89	123.4	776.10	23.72	2.99034
460	462.02	6.245	329.97	211.4	2.13407	1040	1091.85	133.3	793.36	23.29	3.01260
470	472.24	6.742	337.32	200.1	2.15604	1060	1114.86	143.9	810.62	21.14	3.03449
480	482.49	7.268	344.70	189.5	2.17760	1080	1137.89	155.2	827.88	19.98	3.05608
490	492.74	7.824	352.08	179.7	2.19876	1100	1161.07	167.1	845.33	18.896	3.07732
500	503.02	8.411	359.49	170.6	2.21952	1120	1184.28	179.7	862.79	17.886	3.09825
510	513.32	9.031	366.92	162.1	2.23993	1140	1207.57	193.1	880.35	16.946	3.11883
520	523.63	9.684	374.36	154.1	2.25997	1160	1230.92	207.2	897.91	16.064	3.13916
530	533.98	10.37	381.84	146.7	2.27967	1180	1254.34	222.2	915.57	15.241	3.15916
540	544.35	11.10	389.34	139.7	2.29906	1200	1277.79	238.0	933.33	14.470	3.17888
550	555.74	11.86	396.86	133.1	2.31809	1220	1301.31	254.7	951.09	13.747	3.19834
560	565.17	12.66	404.42	127.0	2.33685	1240	1324.93	272.3	968.95	13.069	3.21751
570	575.59	13.50	411.97	121.2	2.35531						

Air

27

TABLE A–17

Ideal-gas properties of air (*Concluded*)

T K	h kJ/kg	P_r	u kJ/kg	v_r	$s°$ kJ/kg · K	T K	h kJ/kg	P_r	u kJ/kg	v_r	$s°$ kJ/kg · K
1260	1348.55	290.8	986.90	12.435	3.23638	1600	1757.57	791.2	1298.30	5.804	3.52364
1280	1372.24	310.4	1004.76	11.835	3.25510	1620	1782.00	834.1	1316.96	5.574	3.53879
1300	1395.97	330.9	1022.82	11.275	3.27345	1640	1806.46	878.9	1335.72	5.355	3.55381
1320	1419.76	352.5	1040.88	10.747	3.29160	1660	1830.96	925.6	1354.48	5.147	3.56867
1340	1443.60	375.3	1058.94	10.247	3.30959	1680	1855.50	974.2	1373.24	4.949	3.58335
1360	1467.49	399.1	1077.10	9.780	3.32724	1700	1880.1	1025	1392.7	4.761	3.5979
1380	1491.44	424.2	1095.26	9.337	3.34474	1750	1941.6	1161	1439.8	4.328	3.6336
1400	1515.42	450.5	1113.52	8.919	3.36200	1800	2003.3	1310	1487.2	3.994	3.6684
1420	1539.44	478.0	1131.77	8.526	3.37901	1850	2065.3	1475	1534.9	3.601	3.7023
1440	1563.51	506.9	1150.13	8.153	3.39586	1900	2127.4	1655	1582.6	3.295	3.7354
1460	1587.63	537.1	1168.49	7.801	3.41247	1950	2189.7	1852	1630.6	3.022	3.7677
1480	1611.79	568.8	1186.95	7.468	3.42892	2000	2252.1	2068	1678.7	2.776	3.7994
1500	1635.97	601.9	1205.41	7.152	3.44516	2050	2314.6	2303	1726.8	2.555	3.8303
1520	1660.23	636.5	1223.87	6.854	3.46120	2100	2377.7	2559	1775.3	2.356	3.8605
1540	1684.51	672.8	1242.43	6.569	3.47712	2150	2440.3	2837	1823.8	2.175	3.8901
1560	1708.82	710.5	1260.99	6.301	3.49276	2200	2503.2	3138	1872.4	2.012	3.9191
1580	1733.17	750.0	1279.65	6.046	3.50829	2250	2566.4	3464	1921.3	1.864	3.9474

Note: The properties P_r (relative pressure) and v_r (relative specific volume) are dimensionless quantities used in the analysis of isentropic processes, and should not be confused with the properties pressure and specific volume.

Source: Kenneth Wark, *Thermodynamics,* 4th ed. (New York: McGraw-Hill, 1983), pp. 785–86, table A–5. Originally published in J. H. Keenan and J. Kaye, *Gas Tables* (New York: John Wiley & Sons, 1948).

Air

Ideal-gas properties of nitrogen, N_2

T K	$\bar{h}$ kJ/kmol	$\bar{u}$ kJ/kmol	$\bar{s}°$ kJ/kmol·K	T K	$\bar{h}$ kJ/kmol	$\bar{u}$ kJ/kmol	$\bar{s}°$ kJ/kmol·K
0	0	0	0	600	17,563	12,574	212.066
220	6,391	4,562	182.639	610	17,864	12,792	212.564
230	6,683	4,770	183.938	620	18,166	13,011	213.055
240	6,975	4,979	185.180	630	18,468	13,230	213.541
250	7,266	5,188	186.370	640	18,772	13,450	214.018
260	7,558	5,396	187.514	650	19,075	13,671	214.489
270	7,849	5,604	188.614	660	19,380	13,892	214.954
280	8,141	5,813	189.673	670	19,685	14,114	215.413
290	8,432	6,021	190.695	680	19,991	14,337	215.866
298	8,669	6,190	191.502	690	20,297	14,560	216.314
300	8,723	6,229	191.682	700	20,604	14,784	216.756
310	9,014	6,437	192.638	710	20,912	15,008	217.192
320	9,306	6,645	193.562	720	21,220	15,234	217.624
330	9,597	6,853	194.459	730	21,529	15,460	218.059
340	9,888	7,061	195.328	740	21,839	15,686	218.472
350	10,180	7,270	196.173	750	22,149	15,913	218.889
360	10,471	7,478	196.995	760	22,460	16,141	219.301
370	10,763	7,687	197.794	770	22,772	16,370	219.709
380	11,055	7,895	198.572	780	23,085	16,599	220.113
390	11,347	8,104	199.331	790	23,398	16,830	220.512
400	11,640	8,314	200.071	800	23,714	17,061	220.907
410	11,932	8,523	200.794	810	24,027	17,292	221.298
420	12,225	8,733	201.499	820	24,342	17,524	221.684
430	12,518	8,943	202.189	830	24,658	17,757	222.067
440	12,811	9,153	202.863	840	24,974	17,990	222.447
450	13,105	9,363	203.523	850	25,292	18,224	222.822
460	13,399	9,574	204.170	860	25,610	18,459	223.194
470	13,693	9,786	204.803	870	25,928	18,695	223.562
480	13,988	9,997	205.424	880	26,248	18,931	223.927
490	14,285	10,210	206.033	890	26,568	19,168	224.288
500	14,581	10,423	206.630	900	26,890	19,407	224.647
510	14,876	10,635	207.216	910	27,210	19,644	225.002
520	15,172	10,848	207.792	920	27,532	19,883	225.353
530	15,469	11,062	208.358	930	27,854	20,122	225.701
540	15,766	11,277	208.914	940	28,178	20,362	226.047
550	16,064	11,492	209.461	950	28,501	20,603	226.389
560	16,363	11,707	209.999	960	28,826	20,844	226.728
570	16,662	11,923	210.528	970	29,151	21,086	227.064
580	16,962	12,139	211.049	980	29,476	21,328	227.398
590	17,262	12,356	211.562	990	29,803	21,571	227.728

N_2

TABLE A–18

Ideal-gas properties of nitrogen, N_2 (*Concluded*)

T K	$\bar{h}$ kJ/kmol	$\bar{u}$ kJ/kmol	$\bar{s}°$ kJ/kmol·K	T K	$\bar{h}$ kJ/kmol	$\bar{u}$ kJ/kmol	$\bar{s}°$ kJ/kmol·K
1000	30,129	21,815	228.057	1760	56,227	41,594	247.396
1020	30,784	22,304	228.706	1780	56,938	42,139	247.798
1040	31,442	22,795	229.344	1800	57,651	42,685	248.195
1060	32,101	23,288	229.973	1820	58,363	43,231	248.589
1080	32,762	23,782	230.591	1840	59,075	43,777	248.979
1100	33,426	24,280	231.199	1860	59,790	44,324	249.365
1120	34,092	24,780	231.799	1880	60,504	44,873	249.748
1140	34,760	25,282	232.391	1900	61,220	45,423	250.128
1160	35,430	25,786	232.973	1920	61,936	45,973	250.502
1180	36,104	26,291	233.549	1940	62,654	46,524	250.874
1200	36,777	26,799	234.115	1960	63,381	47,075	251.242
1220	37,452	27,308	234.673	1980	64,090	47,627	251.607
1240	38,129	27,819	235.223	2000	64,810	48,181	251.969
1260	38,807	28,331	235.766	2050	66,612	49,567	252.858
1280	39,488	28,845	236.302	2100	68,417	50,957	253.726
1300	40,170	29,361	236.831	2150	70,226	52,351	254.578
1320	40,853	29,378	237.353	2200	72,040	53,749	255.412
1340	41,539	30,398	237.867	2250	73,856	55,149	256.227
1360	42,227	30,919	238.376	2300	75,676	56,553	257.027
1380	42,915	31,441	238.878	2350	77,496	57,958	257.810
1400	43,605	31,964	239.375	2400	79,320	59,366	258.580
1420	44,295	32,489	239.865	2450	81,149	60,779	259.332
1440	44,988	33,014	240.350	2500	82,981	62,195	260.073
1460	45,682	33,543	240.827	2550	84,814	63,613	260.799
1480	46,377	34,071	241.301	2600	86,650	65,033	261.512
1500	47,073	34,601	241.768	2650	88,488	66,455	262.213
1520	47,771	35,133	242.228	2700	90,328	67,880	262.902
1540	48,470	35,665	242.685	2750	92,171	69,306	263.577
1560	49,168	36,197	243.137	2800	94,014	70,734	264.241
1580	49,869	36,732	243.585	2850	95,859	72,163	264.895
1600	50,571	37,268	244.028	2900	97,705	73,593	265.538
1620	51,275	37,806	244.464	2950	99,556	75,028	266.170
1640	51,980	38,344	244.896	3000	101,407	76,464	266.793
1660	52,686	38,884	245.324	3050	103,260	77,902	267.404
1680	53,393	39,424	245.747	3100	105,115	79,341	268.007
1700	54,099	39,965	246.166	3150	106,972	80,782	268.601
1720	54,807	40,507	246.580	3200	108,830	82,224	269.186
1740	55,516	41,049	246.990	3250	110,690	83,668	269.763

Source: Tables A–18 through A–25 are adapted from Kenneth Wark, *Thermodynamics,* 4th ed. (New York: McGraw-Hill, 1983), pp. 787–98. Originally published in JANAF, *Thermochemical Tables,* NSRDS-NBS-37, 1971.

TABLE A–19

Ideal-gas properties of oxygen, O_2

T K	$\bar{h}$ kJ/kmol	$\bar{u}$ kJ/kmol	$\bar{s}°$ kJ/kmol·K	T K	$\bar{h}$ kJ/kmol	$\bar{u}$ kJ/kmol	$\bar{s}°$ kJ/kmol·K
0	0	0	0	600	17,929	12,940	226.346
220	6,404	4,575	196.171	610	18,250	13,178	226.877
230	6,694	4,782	197.461	620	18,572	13,417	227.400
240	6,984	4,989	198.696	630	18,895	13,657	227.918
250	7,275	5,197	199.885	640	19,219	13,898	228.429
260	7,566	5,405	201.027	650	19,544	14,140	228.932
270	7,858	5,613	202.128	660	19,870	14,383	229.430
280	8,150	5,822	203.191	670	20,197	14,626	229.920
290	8,443	6,032	204.218	680	20,524	14,871	230.405
298	8,682	6,203	205.033	690	20,854	15,116	230.885
300	8,736	6,242	205.213	700	21,184	15,364	231.358
310	9,030	6,453	206.177	710	21,514	15,611	231.827
320	9,325	6,664	207.112	720	21,845	15,859	232.291
330	9,620	6,877	208.020	730	22,177	16,107	232.748
340	9,916	7,090	208.904	740	22,510	16,357	233.201
350	10,213	7,303	209.765	750	22,844	16,607	233.649
360	10,511	7,518	210.604	760	23,178	16,859	234.091
370	10,809	7,733	211.423	770	23,513	17,111	234.528
380	11,109	7,949	212.222	780	23,850	17,364	234.960
390	11,409	8,166	213.002	790	24,186	17,618	235.387
400	11,711	8,384	213.765	800	24,523	17,872	235.810
410	12,012	8,603	214.510	810	24,861	18,126	236.230
420	12,314	8,822	215.241	820	25,199	18,382	236.644
430	12,618	9,043	215.955	830	25,537	18,637	237.055
440	12,923	9,264	216.656	840	25,877	18,893	237.462
450	13,228	9,487	217.342	850	26,218	19,150	237.864
460	13,525	9,710	218.016	860	26,559	19,408	238.264
470	13,842	9,935	218.676	870	26,899	19,666	238.660
480	14,151	10,160	219.326	880	27,242	19,925	239.051
490	14,460	10,386	219.963	890	27,584	20,185	239.439
500	14,770	10,614	220.589	900	27,928	20,445	239.823
510	15,082	10,842	221.206	910	28,272	20,706	240.203
520	15,395	11,071	221.812	920	28,616	20,967	240.580
530	15,708	11,301	222.409	930	28,960	21,228	240.953
540	16,022	11,533	222.997	940	29,306	21,491	241.323
550	16,338	11,765	223.576	950	29,652	21,754	241.689
560	16,654	11,998	224.146	960	29,999	22,017	242.052
570	16,971	12,232	224.708	970	30,345	22,280	242.411
580	17,290	12,467	225.262	980	30,692	22,544	242.768
590	17,609	12,703	225.808	990	31,041	22,809	242.120

O_2

31

Ideal-gas properties of oxygen, O_2 (*Concluded*)

T	$\bar{h}$	$\bar{u}$	$\bar{s}°$	T	$\bar{h}$	$\bar{u}$	$\bar{s}°$
K	kJ/kmol	kJ/kmol	kJ/kmol·K	K	kJ/kmol	kJ/kmol	kJ/kmol·K
1000	31,389	23,075	243.471	1760	58,880	44,247	263.861
1020	32,088	23,607	244.164	1780	59,624	44,825	264.283
1040	32,789	24,142	244.844	1800	60,371	45,405	264.701
1060	33,490	24,677	245.513	1820	61,118	45,986	265.113
1080	34,194	25,214	246.171	1840	61,866	46,568	265.521
1100	34,899	25,753	246.818	1860	62,616	47,151	265.925
1120	35,606	26,294	247.454	1880	63,365	47,734	266.326
1140	36,314	26,836	248.081	1900	64,116	48,319	266.722
1160	37,023	27,379	248.698	1920	64,868	48,904	267.115
1180	37,734	27,923	249.307	1940	65,620	49,490	267.505
1200	38,447	28,469	249.906	1960	66,374	50,078	267.891
1220	39,162	29,018	250.497	1980	67,127	50,665	268.275
1240	39,877	29,568	251.079	2000	67,881	51,253	268.655
1260	40,594	30,118	251.653	2050	69,772	52,727	269.588
1280	41,312	30,670	252.219	2100	71,668	54,208	270.504
1300	42,033	31,224	252.776	2150	73,573	55,697	271.399
1320	42,753	31,778	253.325	2200	75,484	57,192	272.278
1340	43,475	32,334	253.868	2250	77,397	58,690	273.136
1360	44,198	32,891	254.404	2300	79,316	60,193	273.891
1380	44,923	33,449	254.932	2350	81,243	61,704	274.809
1400	45,648	34,008	255.454	2400	83,174	63,219	275.625
1420	46,374	34,567	255.968	2450	85,112	64,742	276.424
1440	47,102	35,129	256.475	2500	87,057	66,271	277.207
1460	47,831	35,692	256.978	2550	89,004	67,802	277.979
1480	48,561	36,256	257.474	2600	90,956	69,339	278.738
1500	49,292	36,821	257.965	2650	92,916	70,883	279.485
1520	50,024	37,387	258.450	2700	94,881	72,433	280.219
1540	50,756	37,952	258.928	2750	96,852	73,987	280.942
1560	51,490	38,520	259.402	2800	98,826	75,546	281.654
1580	52,224	39,088	259.870	2850	100,808	77,112	282.357
1600	52,961	39,658	260.333	2900	102,793	78,682	283.048
1620	53,696	40,227	260.791	2950	104,785	80,258	283.728
1640	54,434	40,799	261.242	3000	106,780	81,837	284.399
1660	55,172	41,370	261.690	3050	108,778	83,419	285.060
1680	55,912	41,944	262.132	3100	110,784	85,009	285.713
1700	56,652	42,517	262.571	3150	112,795	86,601	286.355
1720	57,394	43,093	263.005	3200	114,809	88,203	286.989
1740	58,136	43,669	263.435	3250	116,827	89,804	287.614

O_2

TABLE A–20

Ideal-gas properties of carbon dioxide, CO_2

T K	$\bar{h}$ kJ/kmol	$\bar{u}$ kJ/kmol	$\bar{s}°$ kJ/kmol·K	T K	$\bar{h}$ kJ/kmol	$\bar{u}$ kJ/kmol	$\bar{s}°$ kJ/kmol·K
0	0	0	0	600	22,280	17,291	243.199
220	6,601	4,772	202.966	610	22,754	17,683	243.983
230	6,938	5,026	204.464	620	23,231	18,076	244.758
240	7,280	5,285	205.920	630	23,709	18,471	245.524
250	7,627	5,548	207.337	640	24,190	18,869	246.282
260	7,979	5,817	208.717	650	24,674	19,270	247.032
270	8,335	6,091	210.062	660	25,160	19,672	247.773
280	8,697	6,369	211.376	670	25,648	20,078	248.507
290	9,063	6,651	212.660	680	26,138	20,484	249.233
298	9,364	6,885	213.685	690	26,631	20,894	249.952
300	9,431	6,939	213.915	700	27,125	21,305	250.663
310	9,807	7,230	215.146	710	27,622	21,719	251.368
320	10,186	7,526	216.351	720	28,121	22,134	252.065
330	10,570	7,826	217.534	730	28,622	22,522	252.755
340	10,959	8,131	218.694	740	29,124	22,972	253.439
350	11,351	8,439	219.831	750	29,629	23,393	254.117
360	11,748	8,752	220.948	760	20,135	23,817	254.787
370	12,148	9,068	222.044	770	30,644	24,242	255.452
380	12,552	9,392	223.122	780	31,154	24,669	256.110
390	12,960	9,718	224.182	790	31,665	25,097	256.762
400	13,372	10,046	225.225	800	32,179	25,527	257.408
410	13,787	10,378	226.250	810	32,694	25,959	258.048
420	14,206	10,714	227.258	820	33,212	26,394	258.682
430	14,628	11,053	228.252	830	33,730	26,829	259.311
440	15,054	11,393	229.230	840	34,251	27,267	259.934
450	15,483	11,742	230.194	850	34,773	27,706	260.551
460	15,916	12,091	231.144	860	35,296	28,125	261.164
470	16,351	12,444	232.080	870	35,821	28,588	261.770
480	16,791	12,800	233.004	880	36,347	29,031	262.371
490	17,232	13,158	233.916	890	36,876	29,476	262.968
500	17,678	13,521	234.814	900	37,405	29,922	263.559
510	18,126	13,885	235.700	910	37,935	30,369	264.146
520	18,576	14,253	236.575	920	38,467	30,818	264.728
530	19,029	14,622	237.439	930	39,000	31,268	265.304
540	19,485	14,996	238.292	940	39,535	31,719	265.877
550	19,945	15,372	239.135	950	40,070	32,171	266.444
560	20,407	15,751	239.962	960	40,607	32,625	267.007
570	20,870	16,131	240.789	970	41,145	33,081	267.566
580	21,337	16,515	241.602	980	41,685	33,537	268.119
590	21,807	16,902	242.405	990	42,226	33,995	268.670

CO_2

TABLE A-20

Ideal-gas properties of carbon dioxide, CO_2 (*Concluded*)

T	$\bar{h}$	$\bar{u}$	$\bar{s}°$	T	$\bar{h}$	$\bar{u}$	$\bar{s}°$
K	kJ/kmol	kJ/kmol	kJ/kmol · K	K	kJ/kmol	kJ/kmol	kJ/kmol · K
1000	42,769	34,455	269.215	1760	86,420	71,787	301.543
1020	43,859	35,378	270.293	1780	87,612	72,812	302.217
1040	44,953	36,306	271.354	1800	88,806	73,840	302.884
1060	46,051	37,238	272.400	1820	90,000	74,868	303.544
1080	47,153	38,174	273.430	1840	91,196	75,897	304.198
1100	48,258	39,112	274.445	1860	92,394	76,929	304.845
1120	49,369	40,057	275.444	1880	93,593	77,962	305.487
1140	50,484	41,006	276.430	1900	94,793	78,996	306.122
1160	51,602	41,957	277.403	1920	95,995	80,031	306.751
1180	52,724	42,913	278.361	1940	97,197	81,067	307.374
1200	53,848	43,871	297.307	1960	98,401	82,105	307.992
1220	54,977	44,834	280.238	1980	99,606	83,144	308.604
1240	56,108	45,799	281.158	2000	100,804	84,185	309.210
1260	57,244	46,768	282.066	2050	103,835	86,791	310.701
1280	58,381	47,739	282.962	2100	106,864	89,404	312.160
1300	59,522	48,713	283.847	2150	109,898	92,023	313.589
1320	60,666	49,691	284.722	2200	112,939	94,648	314.988
1340	61,813	50,672	285.586	2250	115,984	97,277	316.356
1360	62,963	51,656	286.439	2300	119,035	99,912	317.695
1380	64,116	52,643	287.283	2350	122,091	102,552	319.011
1400	65,271	53,631	288.106	2400	125,152	105,197	320.302
1420	66,427	54,621	288.934	2450	128,219	107,849	321.566
1440	67,586	55,614	289.743	2500	131,290	110,504	322.808
1460	68,748	56,609	290.542	2550	134,368	113,166	324.026
1480	66,911	57,606	291.333	2600	137,449	115,832	325.222
1500	71,078	58,606	292.114	2650	140,533	118,500	326.396
1520	72,246	59,609	292.888	2700	143,620	121,172	327.549
1540	73,417	60,613	292.654	2750	146,713	123,849	328.684
1560	74,590	61,620	294.411	2800	149,808	126,528	329.800
1580	76,767	62,630	295.161	2850	152,908	129,212	330.896
1600	76,944	63,741	295.901	2900	156,009	131,898	331.975
1620	78,123	64,653	296.632	2950	159,117	134,589	333.037
1640	79,303	65,668	297.356	3000	162,226	137,283	334.084
1660	80,486	66,592	298.072	3050	165,341	139,982	335.114
1680	81,670	67,702	298.781	3100	168,456	142,681	336.126
1700	82,856	68,721	299.482	3150	171,576	145,385	337.124
1720	84,043	69,742	300.177	3200	174,695	148,089	338.109
1740	85,231	70,764	300.863	3250	177,822	150,801	339.069

CO_2

Ideal-gas properties of carbon monoxide, CO

T K	$\bar{h}$ kJ/kmol	$\bar{u}$ kJ/kmol	$\bar{s}°$ kJ/kmol · K	T K	$\bar{h}$ kJ/kmol	$\bar{u}$ kJ/kmol	$\bar{s}°$ kJ/kmol · K
0	0	0	0	600	17,611	12,622	218.204
220	6,391	4,562	188.683	610	17,915	12,843	218.708
230	6,683	4,771	189.980	620	18,221	13,066	219.205
240	6,975	4,979	191.221	630	18,527	13,289	219.695
250	7,266	5,188	192.411	640	18,833	13,512	220.179
260	7,558	5,396	193.554	650	19,141	13,736	220.656
270	7,849	5,604	194.654	660	19,449	13,962	221.127
280	8,140	5,812	195.713	670	19,758	14,187	221.592
290	8,432	6,020	196.735	680	20,068	14,414	222.052
298	8,669	6,190	197.543	690	20,378	14,641	222.505
300	8,723	6,229	197.723	700	20,690	14,870	222.953
310	9,014	6,437	198.678	710	21,002	15,099	223.396
320	9,306	6,645	199.603	720	21,315	15,328	223.833
330	9,597	6,854	200.500	730	21,628	15,558	224.265
340	9,889	7,062	201.371	740	21,943	15,789	224.692
350	10,181	7,271	202.217	750	22,258	16,022	225.115
360	10,473	7,480	203.040	760	22,573	16,255	225.533
370	10,765	7,689	203.842	770	22,890	16,488	225.947
380	11,058	7,899	204.622	780	23,208	16,723	226.357
390	11,351	8,108	205.383	790	23,526	16,957	226.762
400	11,644	8,319	206.125	800	23,844	17,193	227.162
410	11,938	8,529	206.850	810	24,164	17,429	227.559
420	12,232	8,740	207.549	820	24,483	17,665	227.952
430	12,526	8,951	208.252	830	24,803	17,902	228.339
440	12,821	9,163	208.929	840	25,124	18,140	228.724
450	13,116	9,375	209.593	850	25,446	18,379	229.106
460	13,412	9,587	210.243	860	25,768	18,617	229.482
470	13,708	9,800	210.880	870	26,091	18,858	229.856
480	14,005	10,014	211.504	880	26,415	19,099	230.227
490	14,302	10,228	212.117	890	26,740	19,341	230.593
500	14,600	10,443	212.719	900	27,066	19,583	230.957
510	14,898	10,658	213.310	910	27,392	19,826	231.317
520	15,197	10,874	213.890	920	27,719	20,070	231.674
530	15,497	11,090	214.460	930	28,046	20,314	232.028
540	15,797	11,307	215.020	940	28,375	20,559	232.379
550	16,097	11,524	215.572	950	28,703	20,805	232.727
560	16,399	11,743	216.115	960	29,033	21,051	233.072
570	16,701	11,961	216.649	970	29,362	21,298	233.413
580	17,003	12,181	217.175	980	29,693	21,545	233.752
590	17,307	12,401	217.693	990	30,024	21,793	234.088

CO

Ideal-gas properties of carbon monoxide, CO (*Concluded*)

T K	$\bar{h}$ kJ/kmol	$\bar{u}$ kJ/kmol	$\bar{s}°$ kJ/kmol · K	T K	$\bar{h}$ kJ/kmol	$\bar{u}$ kJ/kmol	$\bar{s}°$ kJ/kmol · K
1000	30,355	22,041	234.421	1760	56,756	42,123	253.991
1020	31,020	22,540	235.079	1780	57,473	42,673	254.398
1040	31,688	23,041	235.728	1800	58,191	43,225	254.797
1060	32,357	23,544	236.364	1820	58,910	43,778	255.194
1080	33,029	24,049	236.992	1840	59,629	44,331	255.587
1100	33,702	24,557	237.609	1860	60,351	44,886	255.976
1120	34,377	25,065	238.217	1880	61,072	45,441	256.361
1140	35,054	25,575	238.817	1900	61,794	45,997	256.743
1160	35,733	26,088	239.407	1920	62,516	46,552	257.122
1180	36,406	26,602	239.989	1940	63,238	47,108	257.497
1200	37,095	27,118	240.663	1960	63,961	47,665	257.868
1220	37,780	27,637	241.128	1980	64,684	48,221	258.236
1240	38,466	28,426	241.686	2000	65,408	48,780	258.600
1260	39,154	28,678	242.236	2050	67,224	50,179	259.494
1280	39,844	29,201	242.780	2100	69,044	51,584	260.370
1300	40,534	29,725	243.316	2150	70,864	52,988	261.226
1320	41,226	30,251	243.844	2200	72,688	54,396	262.065
1340	41,919	30,778	244.366	2250	74,516	55,809	262.887
1360	42,613	31,306	244.880	2300	76,345	57,222	263.692
1380	43,309	31,836	245.388	2350	78,178	58,640	264.480
1400	44,007	32,367	245.889	2400	80,015	60,060	265.253
1420	44,707	32,900	246.385	2450	81,852	61,482	266.012
1440	45,408	33,434	246.876	2500	83,692	62,906	266.755
1460	46,110	33,971	247.360	2550	85,537	64,335	267.485
1480	46,813	34,508	247.839	2600	87,383	65,766	268.202
1500	47,517	35,046	248.312	2650	89,230	67,197	268.905
1520	48,222	35,584	248.778	2700	91,077	68,628	269.596
1540	48,928	36,124	249.240	2750	92,930	70,066	270.285
1560	49,635	36,665	249.695	2800	94,784	71,504	270.943
1580	50,344	37,207	250.147	2850	96,639	72,945	271.602
1600	51,053	37,750	250.592	2900	98,495	74,383	272.249
1620	51,763	38,293	251.033	2950	100,352	75,825	272.884
1640	52,472	38,837	251.470	3000	102,210	77,267	273.508
1660	53,184	39,382	251.901	3050	104,073	78,715	274.123
1680	53,895	39,927	252.329	3100	105,939	80,164	274.730
1700	54,609	40,474	252.751	3150	107,802	81,612	275.326
1720	55,323	41,023	253.169	3200	109,667	83,061	275.914
1740	56,039	41,572	253.582	3250	111,534	84,513	276.494

CO

TABLE A–22

Ideal-gas properties of hydrogen, H_2

T K	$\bar{h}$ kJ/kmol	$\bar{u}$ kJ/kmol	$\bar{s}°$ kJ/kmol · K	T K	$\bar{h}$ kJ/kmol	$\bar{u}$ kJ/kmol	$\bar{s}°$ kJ/kmol · K
0	0	0	0	1440	42,808	30,835	177.410
260	7,370	5,209	126.636	1480	44,091	31,786	178.291
270	7,657	5,412	127.719	1520	45,384	32,746	179.153
280	7,945	5,617	128.765	1560	46,683	33,713	179.995
290	8,233	5,822	129.775	1600	47,990	34,687	180.820
298	8,468	5,989	130.574	1640	49,303	35,668	181.632
300	8,522	6,027	130.754	1680	50,622	36,654	182.428
320	9,100	6,440	132.621	1720	51,947	37,646	183.208
340	9,680	6,853	134.378	1760	53,279	38,645	183.973
360	10,262	7,268	136.039	1800	54,618	39,652	184.724
380	10,843	7,684	137.612	1840	55,962	40,663	185.463
400	11,426	8,100	139.106	1880	57,311	41,680	186.190
420	12,010	8,518	140.529	1920	58,668	42,705	186.904
440	12,594	8,936	141.888	1960	60,031	43,735	187.607
460	13,179	9,355	143.187	2000	61,400	44,771	188.297
480	13,764	9,773	144.432	2050	63,119	46,074	189.148
500	14,350	10,193	145.628	2100	64,847	47,386	189.979
520	14,935	10,611	146.775	2150	66,584	48,708	190.796
560	16,107	11,451	148.945	2200	68,328	50,037	191.598
600	17,280	12,291	150.968	2250	70,080	51,373	192.385
640	18,453	13,133	152.863	2300	71,839	52,716	193.159
680	19,630	13,976	154.645	2350	73,608	54,069	193.921
720	20,807	14,821	156.328	2400	75,383	55,429	194.669
760	21,988	15,669	157.923	2450	77,168	56,798	195.403
800	23,171	16,520	159.440	2500	78,960	58,175	196.125
840	24,359	17,375	160.891	2550	80,755	59,554	196.837
880	25,551	18,235	162.277	2600	82,558	60,941	197.539
920	26,747	19,098	163.607	2650	84,368	62,335	198.229
960	27,948	19,966	164.884	2700	86,186	63,737	198.907
1000	29,154	20,839	166.114	2750	88,008	65,144	199.575
1040	30,364	21,717	167.300	2800	89,838	66,558	200.234
1080	31,580	22,601	168.449	2850	91,671	67,976	200.885
1120	32,802	23,490	169.560	2900	93,512	69,401	201.527
1160	34,028	24,384	170.636	2950	95,358	70,831	202.157
1200	35,262	25,284	171.682	3000	97,211	72,268	202.778
1240	36,502	26,192	172.698	3050	99,065	73,707	203.391
1280	37,749	27,106	173.687	3100	100,926	75,152	203.995
1320	39,002	28,027	174.652	3150	102,793	76,604	204.592
1360	40,263	28,955	175.593	3200	104,667	78,061	205.181
1400	41,530	29,889	176.510	3250	106,545	79,523	205.765

TABLE A–23

Ideal-gas properties of water vapor, H_2O

T K	$\bar{h}$ kJ/kmol	$\bar{u}$ kJ/kmol	$\bar{s}°$ kJ/kmol·K	T K	$\bar{h}$ kJ/kmol	$\bar{u}$ kJ/kmol	$\bar{s}°$ kJ/kmol·K
0	0	0	0	600	20,402	15,413	212.920
220	7,295	5,466	178.576	610	20,765	15,693	213.529
230	7,628	5,715	180.054	620	21,130	15,975	214.122
240	7,961	5,965	181.471	630	21,495	16,257	214.707
250	8,294	6,215	182.831	640	21,862	16,541	215.285
260	8,627	6,466	184.139	650	22,230	16,826	215.856
270	8,961	6,716	185.399	660	22,600	17,112	216.419
280	9,296	6,968	186.616	670	22,970	17,399	216.976
290	9,631	7,219	187.791	680	23,342	17,688	217.527
298	9,904	7,425	188.720	690	23,714	17,978	218.071
300	9,966	7,472	188.928	700	24,088	18,268	218.610
310	10,302	7,725	190.030	710	24,464	18,561	219.142
320	10,639	7,978	191.098	720	24,840	18,854	219.668
330	10,976	8,232	192.136	730	25,218	19,148	220.189
340	11,314	8,487	193.144	740	25,597	19,444	220.707
350	11,652	8,742	194.125	750	25,977	19,741	221.215
360	11,992	8,998	195.081	760	26,358	20,039	221.720
370	12,331	9,255	196.012	770	26,741	20,339	222.221
380	12,672	9,513	196.920	780	27,125	20,639	222.717
390	13,014	9,771	197.807	790	27,510	20,941	223.207
400	13,356	10,030	198.673	800	27,896	21,245	223.693
410	13,699	10,290	199.521	810	28,284	21,549	224.174
420	14,043	10,551	200.350	820	28,672	21,855	224.651
430	14,388	10,813	201.160	830	29,062	22,162	225.123
440	14,734	11,075	201.955	840	29,454	22,470	225.592
450	15,080	11,339	202.734	850	29,846	22,779	226.057
460	15,428	11,603	203.497	860	30,240	23,090	226.517
470	15,777	11,869	204.247	870	30,635	23,402	226.973
480	16,126	12,135	204.982	880	31,032	23,715	227.426
490	16,477	12,403	205.705	890	31,429	24,029	227.875
500	16,828	12,671	206.413	900	31,828	24,345	228.321
510	17,181	12,940	207.112	910	32,228	24,662	228.763
520	17,534	13,211	207.799	920	32,629	24,980	229.202
530	17,889	13,482	208.475	930	33,032	25,300	229.637
540	18,245	13,755	209.139	940	33,436	25,621	230.070
550	18,601	14,028	209.795	950	33,841	25,943	230.499
560	18,959	14,303	210.440	960	34,247	26,265	230.924
570	19,318	14,579	211.075	970	34,653	26,588	231.347
580	19,678	14,856	211.702	980	35,061	26,913	231.767
590	20,039	15,134	212.320	990	35,472	27,240	232.184

Ideal-gas properties of water vapor, H_2O (*Concluded*)

T	$\bar{h}$	$\bar{u}$	$\bar{s}°$	T	$\bar{h}$	$\bar{u}$	$\bar{s}°$
K	kJ/kmol	kJ/kmol	kJ/kmol·K	K	kJ/kmol	kJ/kmol	kJ/kmol·K
1000	35,882	27,568	232.597	1760	70,535	55,902	258.151
1020	36,709	28,228	233.415	1780	71,523	56,723	258.708
1040	37,542	28,895	234.223	1800	72,513	57,547	259.262
1060	38,380	29,567	235.020	1820	73,507	58,375	259.811
1080	39,223	30,243	235.806	1840	74,506	59,207	260.357
1100	40,071	30,925	236.584	1860	75,506	60,042	260.898
1120	40,923	31,611	237.352	1880	76,511	60,880	261.436
1140	41,780	32,301	238.110	1900	77,517	61,720	261.969
1160	42,642	32,997	238.859	1920	78,527	62,564	262.497
1180	43,509	33,698	239.600	1940	79,540	63,411	263.022
1200	44,380	34,403	240.333	1960	80,555	64,259	263.542
1220	45,256	35,112	241.057	1980	81,573	65,111	264.059
1240	46,137	35,827	241.773	2000	82,593	65,965	264.571
1260	47,022	36,546	242.482	2050	85,156	68,111	265.838
1280	47,912	37,270	243.183	2100	87,735	70,275	267.081
1300	48,807	38,000	243.877	2150	90,330	72,454	268.301
1320	49,707	38,732	244.564	2200	92,940	74,649	269.500
1340	50,612	39,470	245.243	2250	95,562	76,855	270.679
1360	51,521	40,213	245.915	2300	98,199	79,076	271.839
1380	52,434	40,960	246.582	2350	100,846	81,308	272.978
1400	53,351	41,711	247.241	2400	103,508	83,553	274.098
1420	54,273	42,466	247.895	2450	106,183	85,811	275.201
1440	55,198	43,226	248.543	2500	108,868	88,082	276.286
1460	56,128	43,989	249.185	2550	111,565	90,364	277.354
1480	57,062	44,756	249.820	2600	114,273	92,656	278.407
1500	57,999	45,528	250.450	2650	116,991	94,958	279.441
1520	58,942	46,304	251.074	2700	119,717	97,269	280.462
1540	59,888	47,084	251.693	2750	122,453	99,588	281.464
1560	60,838	47,868	252.305	2800	125,198	101,917	282.453
1580	61,792	48,655	252.912	2850	127,952	104,256	283.429
1600	62,748	49,445	253.513	2900	130,717	106,605	284.390
1620	63,709	50,240	254.111	2950	133,486	108,959	285.338
1640	64,675	51,039	254.703	3000	136,264	111,321	286.273
1660	65,643	51,841	255.290	3050	139,051	113,692	287.194
1680	66,614	52,646	255.873	3100	141,846	116,072	288.102
1700	67,589	53,455	256.450	3150	144,648	118,458	288.999
1720	68,567	54,267	257.022	3200	147,457	120,851	289.884
1740	69,550	55,083	257.589	3250	150,272	123,250	290.756

H_2O

TABLE A–24

Ideal-gas properties of monatomic oxygen, O

<table>
<tr><td>T
K</td><td>$\bar{h}$
kJ/kmol</td><td>$\bar{u}$
kJ/kmol</td><td>$\bar{s}°$
kJ/kmol·K</td><td>T
K</td><td>$\bar{h}$
kJ/kmol</td><td>$\bar{u}$
kJ/kmol</td><td>$\bar{s}°$
kJ/kmol·K</td></tr>
<tr><td>0</td><td>0</td><td>0</td><td>0</td><td>2400</td><td>50,894</td><td>30,940</td><td>204.932</td></tr>
<tr><td>298</td><td>6,852</td><td>4,373</td><td>160.944</td><td>2450</td><td>51,936</td><td>31,566</td><td>205.362</td></tr>
<tr><td>300</td><td>6,892</td><td>4,398</td><td>161.079</td><td>2500</td><td>52,979</td><td>32,193</td><td>205.783</td></tr>
<tr><td>500</td><td>11,197</td><td>7,040</td><td>172.088</td><td>2550</td><td>54,021</td><td>32,820</td><td>206.196</td></tr>
<tr><td>1000</td><td>21,713</td><td>13,398</td><td>186.678</td><td>2600</td><td>55,064</td><td>33,447</td><td>206.601</td></tr>
<tr><td>1500</td><td>32,150</td><td>19,679</td><td>195.143</td><td>2650</td><td>56,108</td><td>34,075</td><td>206.999</td></tr>
<tr><td>1600</td><td>34,234</td><td>20,931</td><td>196.488</td><td>2700</td><td>57,152</td><td>34,703</td><td>207.389</td></tr>
<tr><td>1700</td><td>36,317</td><td>22,183</td><td>197.751</td><td>2750</td><td>58,196</td><td>35,332</td><td>207.772</td></tr>
<tr><td>1800</td><td>38,400</td><td>23,434</td><td>198.941</td><td>2800</td><td>59,241</td><td>35,961</td><td>208.148</td></tr>
<tr><td>1900</td><td>40,482</td><td>24,685</td><td>200.067</td><td>2850</td><td>60,286</td><td>36,590</td><td>208.518</td></tr>
<tr><td>2000</td><td>42,564</td><td>25,935</td><td>201.135</td><td>2900</td><td>61,332</td><td>37,220</td><td>208.882</td></tr>
<tr><td>2050</td><td>43,605</td><td>26,560</td><td>201.649</td><td>2950</td><td>62,378</td><td>37,851</td><td>209.240</td></tr>
<tr><td>2100</td><td>44,646</td><td>27,186</td><td>202.151</td><td>3000</td><td>63,425</td><td>38,482</td><td>209.592</td></tr>
<tr><td>2150</td><td>45,687</td><td>27,811</td><td>202.641</td><td>3100</td><td>65,520</td><td>39,746</td><td>210.279</td></tr>
<tr><td>2200</td><td>46,728</td><td>28,436</td><td>203.119</td><td>3200</td><td>67,619</td><td>41,013</td><td>210.945</td></tr>
<tr><td>2250</td><td>47,769</td><td>29,062</td><td>203.588</td><td>3300</td><td>69,720</td><td>42,283</td><td>211.592</td></tr>
<tr><td>2300</td><td>48,811</td><td>29,688</td><td>204.045</td><td>3400</td><td>71,824</td><td>43,556</td><td>212.220</td></tr>
<tr><td>2350</td><td>49,852</td><td>30,314</td><td>204.493</td><td>3500</td><td>73,932</td><td>44,832</td><td>212.831</td></tr>
</table>

TABLE A–25

Ideal-gas properties of hydroxyl, OH

<table>
<tr><td>T
K</td><td>$\bar{h}$
kJ/kmol</td><td>$\bar{u}$
kJ/kmol</td><td>$\bar{s}°$
kJ/kmol·K</td><td>T
K</td><td>$\bar{h}$
kJ/kmol</td><td>$\bar{u}$
kJ/kmol</td><td>$\bar{s}°$
kJ/kmol·K</td></tr>
<tr><td>0</td><td>0</td><td>0</td><td>0</td><td>2400</td><td>77,015</td><td>57,061</td><td>248.628</td></tr>
<tr><td>298</td><td>9,188</td><td>6,709</td><td>183.594</td><td>2450</td><td>78,801</td><td>58,431</td><td>249.364</td></tr>
<tr><td>300</td><td>9,244</td><td>6,749</td><td>183.779</td><td>2500</td><td>80,592</td><td>59,806</td><td>250.088</td></tr>
<tr><td>500</td><td>15,181</td><td>11,024</td><td>198.955</td><td>2550</td><td>82,388</td><td>61,186</td><td>250.799</td></tr>
<tr><td>1000</td><td>30,123</td><td>21,809</td><td>219.624</td><td>2600</td><td>84,189</td><td>62,572</td><td>251.499</td></tr>
<tr><td>1500</td><td>46,046</td><td>33,575</td><td>232.506</td><td>2650</td><td>85,995</td><td>63,962</td><td>252.187</td></tr>
<tr><td>1600</td><td>49,358</td><td>36,055</td><td>234.642</td><td>2700</td><td>87,806</td><td>65,358</td><td>252.864</td></tr>
<tr><td>1700</td><td>52,706</td><td>38,571</td><td>236.672</td><td>2750</td><td>89,622</td><td>66,757</td><td>253.530</td></tr>
<tr><td>1800</td><td>56,089</td><td>41,123</td><td>238.606</td><td>2800</td><td>91,442</td><td>68,162</td><td>254.186</td></tr>
<tr><td>1900</td><td>59,505</td><td>43,708</td><td>240.453</td><td>2850</td><td>93,266</td><td>69,570</td><td>254.832</td></tr>
<tr><td>2000</td><td>62,952</td><td>46,323</td><td>242.221</td><td>2900</td><td>95,095</td><td>70,983</td><td>255.468</td></tr>
<tr><td>2050</td><td>64,687</td><td>47,642</td><td>243.077</td><td>2950</td><td>96,927</td><td>72,400</td><td>256.094</td></tr>
<tr><td>2100</td><td>66,428</td><td>48,968</td><td>243.917</td><td>3000</td><td>98,763</td><td>73,820</td><td>256.712</td></tr>
<tr><td>2150</td><td>68,177</td><td>50,301</td><td>244.740</td><td>3100</td><td>102,447</td><td>76,673</td><td>257.919</td></tr>
<tr><td>2200</td><td>69,932</td><td>51,641</td><td>245.547</td><td>3200</td><td>106,145</td><td>79,539</td><td>259.093</td></tr>
<tr><td>2250</td><td>71,694</td><td>52,987</td><td>246.338</td><td>3300</td><td>109,855</td><td>82,418</td><td>260.235</td></tr>
<tr><td>2300</td><td>73,462</td><td>54,339</td><td>247.116</td><td>3400</td><td>113,578</td><td>85,309</td><td>261.347</td></tr>
<tr><td>2350</td><td>75,236</td><td>55,697</td><td>247.879</td><td>3500</td><td>117,312</td><td>88,212</td><td>262.429</td></tr>
</table>

O, OH

TABLE A–26

Enthalpy of formation, Gibbs function of formation, and absolute entropy at 25°C, 1 atm

Substance	Formula	$\bar{h}_f^{\circ}$ kJ/kmol	$\bar{g}_f^{\circ}$ kJ/kmol	$\bar{s}^{\circ}$ kJ/kmol · K
Carbon	C(s)	0	0	5.74
Hydrogen	$H_2(g)$	0	0	130.68
Nitrogen	$N_2(g)$	0	0	191.61
Oxygen	$O_2(g)$	0	0	205.04
Carbon monoxide	CO(g)	−110,530	−137,150	197.65
Carbon dioxide	$CO_2(g)$	−393,520	−394,360	213.80
Water vapor	$H_2O(g)$	−241,820	−228,590	188.83
Water	$H_2O(\ell)$	−285,830	−237,180	69.92
Hydrogen peroxide	$H_2O_2(g)$	−136,310	−105,600	232.63
Ammonia	$NH_3(g)$	−46,190	−16,590	192.33
Methane	$CH_4(g)$	−74,850	−50,790	186.16
Acetylene	$C_2H_2(g)$	+226,730	+209,170	200.85
Ethylene	$C_2H_4(g)$	+52,280	+68,120	219.83
Ethane	$C_2H_6(g)$	−84,680	−32,890	229.49
Propylene	$C_3H_6(g)$	+20,410	+62,720	266.94
Propane	$C_3H_8(g)$	−103,850	−23,490	269.91
n-Butane	$C_4H_{10}(g)$	−126,150	−15,710	310.12
n-Octane	$C_8H_{18}(g)$	−208,450	+16,530	466.73
n-Octane	$C_8H_{18}(\ell)$	−249,950	+6,610	360.79
n-Dodecane	$C_{12}H_{26}(g)$	−291,010	+50,150	622.83
Benzene	$C_6H_6(g)$	+82,930	+129,660	269.20
Methyl alcohol	$CH_3OH(g)$	−200,670	−162,000	239.70
Methyl alcohol	$CH_3OH(\ell)$	−238,660	−166,360	126.80
Ethyl alcohol	$C_2H_5OH(g)$	−235,310	−168,570	282.59
Ethyl alcohol	$C_2H_5OH(\ell)$	−277,690	−174,890	160.70
Oxygen	O(g)	+249,190	+231,770	161.06
Hydrogen	H(g)	+218,000	+203,290	114.72
Nitrogen	N(g)	+472,650	+455,510	153.30
Hydroxyl	OH(g)	+39,460	+34,280	183.70

Source: From JANAF, *Thermochemical Tables* (Midland, MI: Dow Chemical Co., 1971); *Selected Values of Chemical Thermodynamic Properties,* NBS Technical Note 270-3, 1968; and *API Research Project 44* (Carnegie Press, 1953).

TABLE A–27

Properties of some common fuels and hydrocarbons

Fuel (phase)	Formula	Molar mass, kg/kmol	Density,[1] kg/L	Enthalpy of vaporization,[2] kJ/kg	Specific heat,[1] c_p kJ/kg · K	Higher heating value,[3] kJ/kg	Lower heating value,[3] kJ/kg
Carbon (s)	C	12.011	2	—	0.708	32,800	32,800
Hydrogen (g)	H_2	2.016	—	—	14.4	141,800	120,000
Carbon monoxide (g)	CO	28.013	—	—	1.05	10,100	10,100
Methane (g)	CH_4	16.043	—	509	2.20	55,530	50,050
Methanol (ℓ)	CH_4O	32.042	0.790	1168	2.53	22,660	19,920
Acetylene (g)	C_2H_2	26.038	—	—	1.69	49,970	48,280
Ethane (g)	C_2H_6	30.070	—	172	1.75	51,900	47,520
Ethanol (ℓ)	C_2H_6O	46.069	0.790	919	2.44	29,670	26,810
Propane (ℓ)	C_3H_8	44.097	0.500	335	2.77	50,330	46,340
Butane (ℓ)	C_4H_{10}	58.123	0.579	362	2.42	49,150	45,370
1-Pentene (ℓ)	C_5H_{10}	70.134	0.641	363	2.20	47,760	44,630
Isopentane (ℓ)	C_5H_{12}	72.150	0.626	—	2.32	48,570	44,910
Benzene (ℓ)	C_6H_6	78.114	0.877	433	1.72	41,800	40,100
Hexene (ℓ)	C_6H_{12}	84.161	0.673	392	1.84	47,500	44,400
Hexane (ℓ)	C_6H_{14}	86.177	0.660	366	2.27	48,310	44,740
Toluene (ℓ)	C_7H_8	92.141	0.867	412	1.71	42,400	40,500
Heptane (ℓ)	C_7H_{16}	100.204	0.684	365	2.24	48,100	44,600
Octane (ℓ)	C_8H_{18}	114.231	0.703	363	2.23	47,890	44,430
Decane (ℓ)	$C_{10}H_{22}$	142.285	0.730	361	2.21	47,640	44,240
Gasoline (ℓ)	$C_nH_{1.87n}$	100–110	0.72–0.78	350	2.4	47,300	44,000
Light diesel (ℓ)	$C_nH_{1.8n}$	170	0.78–0.84	270	2.2	46,100	43,200
Heavy diesel (ℓ)	$C_nH_{1.7n}$	200	0.82–0.88	230	1.9	45,500	42,800
Natural gas (g)	$C_nH_{3.8n}N_{0.1n}$	18	—	—	2	50,000	45,000

[1]At 1 atm and 20°C.

[2]At 25°C for liquid fuels, and 1 atm and normal boiling temperature for gaseous fuels.

[3]At 25°C. Multiply by molar mass to obtain heating values in kJ/kmol.

Natural logarithms of the equilibrium constant K_p

The equilibrium constant K_p for the reaction $\nu_A A + \nu_B B \rightleftharpoons \nu_C C + \nu_D D$ is defined as $K_p \equiv \dfrac{P_C^{\nu_C} P_D^{\nu_D}}{P_A^{\nu_A} P_B^{\nu_B}}$

Temp., K	$H_2 \rightleftharpoons 2H$	$O_2 \rightleftharpoons 2O$	$N_2 \rightleftharpoons 2N$	$H_2O \rightleftharpoons H_2 + {}^{1}/_2 O_2$	$H_2O \rightleftharpoons {}^{1}/_2 H_2 + OH$	$CO_2 \rightleftharpoons CO + {}^{1}/_2 O_2$	${}^{1}/_2 N_2 + {}^{1}/_2 O_2 \rightleftharpoons NO$
298	−164.005	−186.975	−367.480	−92.208	−106.208	−103.762	−35.052
500	−92.827	−105.630	−213.372	−52.691	−60.281	−57.616	−20.295
1000	−39.803	−45.150	−99.127	−23.163	−26.034	−23.529	−9.388
1200	−30.874	−35.005	−80.011	−18.182	−20.283	−17.871	−7.569
1400	−24.463	−27.742	−66.329	−14.609	−16.099	−13.842	−6.270
1600	−19.637	−22.285	−56.055	−11.921	−13.066	−10.830	−5.294
1800	−15.866	−18.030	−48.051	−9.826	−10.657	−8.497	−4.536
2000	−12.840	−14.622	−41.645	−8.145	−8.728	−6.635	−3.931
2200	−10.353	−11.827	−36.391	−6.768	−7.148	−5.120	−3.433
2400	−8.276	−9.497	−32.011	−5.619	−5.832	−3.860	−3.019
2600	−6.517	−7.521	−28.304	−4.648	−4.719	−2.801	−2.671
2800	−5.002	−5.826	−25.117	−3.812	−3.763	−1.894	−2.372
3000	−3.685	−4.357	−22.359	−3.086	−2.937	−1.111	−2.114
3200	−2.534	−3.072	−19.937	−2.451	−2.212	−0.429	−1.888
3400	−1.516	−1.935	−17.800	−1.891	−1.576	0.169	−1.690
3600	−0.609	−0.926	−15.898	−1.392	−1.088	0.701	−1.513
3800	0.202	−0.019	−14.199	−0.945	−0.501	1.176	−1.356
4000	0.934	0.796	−12.660	−0.542	−0.044	1.599	−1.216
4500	2.486	2.513	−9.414	0.312	0.920	2.490	−0.921
5000	3.725	3.895	−6.807	0.996	1.689	3.197	−0.686
5500	4.743	5.023	−4.666	1.560	2.318	3.771	−0.497
6000	5.590	5.963	−2.865	2.032	2.843	4.245	−0.341

Source: Gordon J. Van Wylen and Richard E. Sonntag, *Fundamentals of Classical Thermodynamics,* English/SI Version, 3rd ed. (New York: John Wiley & Sons, 1986), p. 723, table A.14. Based on thermodynamic data given in JANAF, *Thermochemical Tables* (Midland, MI: Thermal Research Laboratory, The Dow Chemical Company, 1971).

K_p

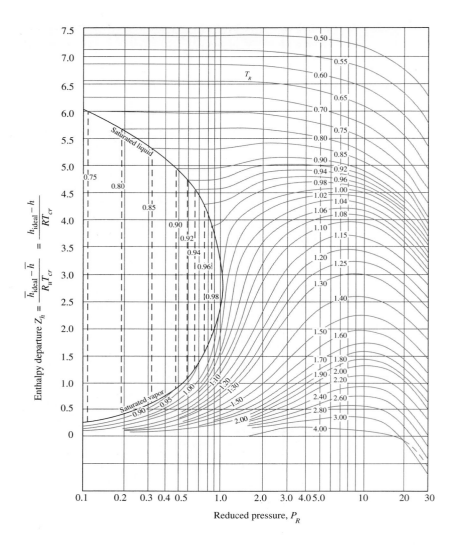

FIGURE A–29

Generalized enthalpy departure chart.

Source: John R. Howell and Richard O. Buckius, Fundamentals of Engineering Thermodynamics, SI Version (New York: McGraw-Hill, 1987), p. 558, fig. C.2, and p. 561, fig. C.5.

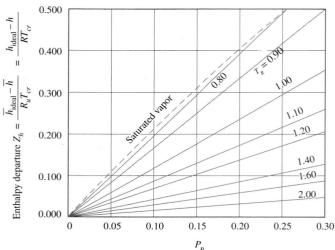

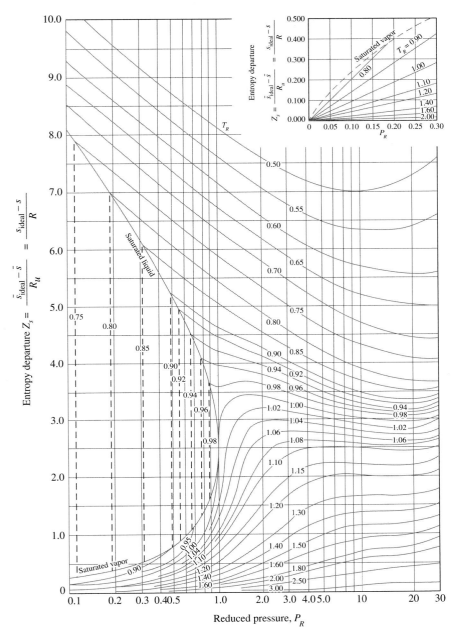

FIGURE A–30

Generalized entropy departure chart.

Source: John R. Howell and Richard O. Buckius, Fundamentals of Engineering Thermodynamics, *SI Version (New York: McGraw-Hill, 1987), p. 559, fig. C.3, and p. 561, fig. C.5.*

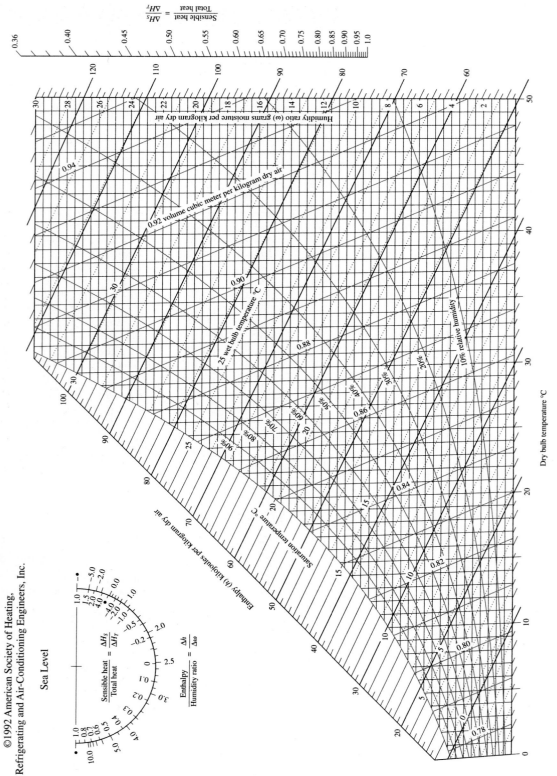

Prepared by Center for Applied Thermodynamic Studies, University of Idaho.

FIGURE A–31

Psychrometric chart at 1 atm total pressure.

Reprinted by permission of the American Society of Heating, Refrigerating and Air-Conditioning Engineers, Inc., Atlanta, GA; used with permission.

$$\text{Ma}^* = \text{Ma}\sqrt{\frac{k+1}{2+(k-1)\text{Ma}^2}}$$

$$\frac{A}{A^*} = \frac{1}{\text{Ma}}\left[\left(\frac{2}{k+1}\right)\left(1+\frac{k-1}{2}\text{Ma}^2\right)\right]^{0.5(k+1)/(k-1)}$$

$$\frac{P}{P_0} = \left(1+\frac{k-1}{2}\text{Ma}^2\right)^{-k/(k-1)}$$

$$\frac{\rho}{\rho_0} = \left(1+\frac{k-1}{2}\text{Ma}^2\right)^{-1/(k-1)}$$

$$\frac{T}{T_0} = \left(1+\frac{k-1}{2}\text{Ma}^2\right)^{-1}$$

TABLE A–32

One-dimensional isentropic compressible flow functions for an ideal gas with $k = 1.4$

Ma	Ma*	A/A*	P/P_0	ρ/ρ_0	T/T_0
0	0	∞	1.0000	1.0000	1.0000
0.1	0.1094	5.8218	0.9930	0.9950	0.9980
0.2	0.2182	2.9635	0.9725	0.9803	0.9921
0.3	0.3257	2.0351	0.9395	0.9564	0.9823
0.4	0.4313	1.5901	0.8956	0.9243	0.9690
0.5	0.5345	1.3398	0.8430	0.8852	0.9524
0.6	0.6348	1.1882	0.7840	0.8405	0.9328
0.7	0.7318	1.0944	0.7209	0.7916	0.9107
0.8	0.8251	1.0382	0.6560	0.7400	0.8865
0.9	0.9146	1.0089	0.5913	0.6870	0.8606
1.0	1.0000	1.0000	0.5283	0.6339	0.8333
1.2	1.1583	1.0304	0.4124	0.5311	0.7764
1.4	1.2999	1.1149	0.3142	0.4374	0.7184
1.6	1.4254	1.2502	0.2353	0.3557	0.6614
1.8	1.5360	1.4390	0.1740	0.2868	0.6068
2.0	1.6330	1.6875	0.1278	0.2300	0.5556
2.2	1.7179	2.0050	0.0935	0.1841	0.5081
2.4	1.7922	2.4031	0.0684	0.1472	0.4647
2.6	1.8571	2.8960	0.0501	0.1179	0.4252
2.8	1.9140	3.5001	0.0368	0.0946	0.3894
3.0	1.9640	4.2346	0.0272	0.0760	0.3571
5.0	2.2361	25.000	0.0019	0.0113	0.1667
∞	2.2495	∞	0	0	0

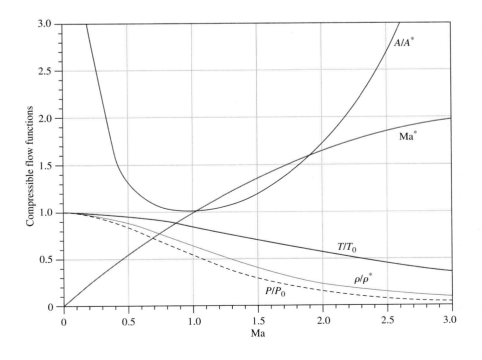

$$T_{01} = T_{02}$$

$$Ma_2 = \sqrt{\frac{(k-1)Ma_1^2 + 2}{2kMa_1^2 - k + 1}}$$

$$\frac{P_2}{P_1} = \frac{1 + kMa_1^2}{1 + kMa_2^2} = \frac{2kMa_1^2 - k + 1}{k + 1}$$

$$\frac{\rho_2}{\rho_1} = \frac{P_2/P_1}{T_2/T_1} = \frac{(k+1)Ma_1^2}{2 + (k-1)Ma_1^2} = \frac{V_1}{V_2}$$

$$\frac{T_2}{T_1} = \frac{2 + Ma_1^2(k-1)}{2 + Ma_2^2(k-1)}$$

$$\frac{P_{02}}{P_{01}} = \frac{Ma_1}{Ma_2}\left[\frac{1 + Ma_2^2(k-1)/2}{1 + Ma_1^2(k-1)/2}\right]^{(k+1)/[2(k-1)]}$$

$$\frac{P_{02}}{P_1} = \frac{(1 + kMa_1^2)[1 + Ma_2^2(k-1)/2]^{k/(k-1)}}{1 + kMa_2^2}$$

TABLE A–33

One-dimensional normal shock functions for an ideal gas with $k = 1.4$

Ma_1	Ma_2	P_2/P_1	ρ_2/ρ_1	T_2/T_1	P_{02}/P_{01}	P_{02}/P_1
1.0	1.0000	1.0000	1.0000	1.0000	1.0000	1.8929
1.1	0.9118	1.2450	1.1691	1.0649	0.9989	2.1328
1.2	0.8422	1.5133	1.3416	1.1280	0.9928	2.4075
1.3	0.7860	1.8050	1.5157	1.1909	0.9794	2.7136
1.4	0.7397	2.1200	1.6897	1.2547	0.9582	3.0492
1.5	0.7011	2.4583	1.8621	1.3202	0.9298	3.4133
1.6	0.6684	2.8200	2.0317	1.3880	0.8952	3.8050
1.7	0.6405	3.2050	2.1977	1.4583	0.8557	4.2238
1.8	0.6165	3.6133	2.3592	1.5316	0.8127	4.6695
1.9	0.5956	4.0450	2.5157	1.6079	0.7674	5.1418
2.0	0.5774	4.5000	2.6667	1.6875	0.7209	5.6404
2.1	0.5613	4.9783	2.8119	1.7705	0.6742	6.1654
2.2	0.5471	5.4800	2.9512	1.8569	0.6281	6.7165
2.3	0.5344	6.0050	3.0845	1.9468	0.5833	7.2937
2.4	0.5231	6.5533	3.2119	2.0403	0.5401	7.8969
2.5	0.5130	7.1250	3.3333	2.1375	0.4990	8.5261
2.6	0.5039	7.7200	3.4490	2.2383	0.4601	9.1813
2.7	0.4956	8.3383	3.5590	2.3429	0.4236	9.8624
2.8	0.4882	8.9800	3.6636	2.4512	0.3895	10.5694
2.9	0.4814	9.6450	3.7629	2.5632	0.3577	11.3022
3.0	0.4752	10.3333	3.8571	2.6790	0.3283	12.0610
4.0	0.4350	18.5000	4.5714	4.0469	0.1388	21.0681
5.0	0.4152	29.000	5.0000	5.8000	0.0617	32.6335
∞	0.3780	∞	6.0000	∞	0	∞

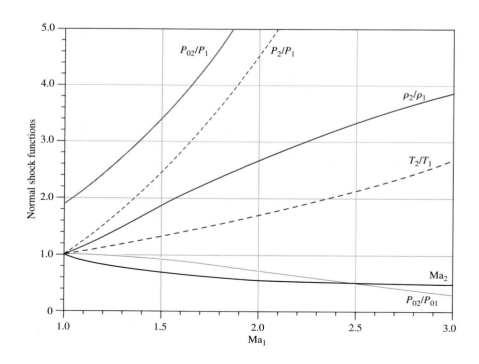

$$\frac{T_0}{T_0^*} = \frac{(k + 1)\text{Ma}^2[2 + (k - 1)\text{Ma}^2]}{(1 + k\text{Ma}^2)^2}$$

$$\frac{P_0}{P_0^*} = \frac{k + 1}{1 + k\text{Ma}^2}\left(\frac{2 + (k - 1)\text{Ma}^2}{k + 1}\right)^{k/(k-1)}$$

$$\frac{T}{T^*} = \left(\frac{\text{Ma}(1 + k)}{1 + k\text{Ma}^2}\right)^2$$

$$\frac{P}{P^*} = \frac{1 + k}{1 + k\text{Ma}^2}$$

$$\frac{V}{V^*} = \frac{\rho^*}{\rho} = \frac{(1 + k)\text{Ma}^2}{1 + k\text{Ma}^2}$$

TABLE A–34

Rayleigh flow functions for an ideal gas with $k = 1.4$

Ma	T_0/T_0^*	P_0/P_0^*	T/T^*	P/P^*	V/V^*
0.0	0.0000	1.2679	0.0000	2.4000	0.0000
0.1	0.0468	1.2591	0.0560	2.3669	0.0237
0.2	0.1736	1.2346	0.2066	2.2727	0.0909
0.3	0.3469	1.1985	0.4089	2.1314	0.1918
0.4	0.5290	1.1566	0.6151	1.9608	0.3137
0.5	0.6914	1.1141	0.7901	1.7778	0.4444
0.6	0.8189	1.0753	0.9167	1.5957	0.5745
0.7	0.9085	1.0431	0.9929	1.4235	0.6975
0.8	0.9639	1.0193	1.0255	1.2658	0.8101
0.9	0.9921	1.0049	1.0245	1.1246	0.9110
1.0	1.0000	1.0000	1.0000	1.0000	1.0000
1.2	0.9787	1.0194	0.9118	0.7958	1.1459
1.4	0.9343	1.0777	0.8054	0.6410	1.2564
1.6	0.8842	1.1756	0.7017	0.5236	1.3403
1.8	0.8363	1.3159	0.6089	0.4335	1.4046
2.0	0.7934	1.5031	0.5289	0.3636	1.4545
2.2	0.7561	1.7434	0.4611	0.3086	1.4938
2.4	0.7242	2.0451	0.4038	0.2648	1.5252
2.6	0.6970	2.4177	0.3556	0.2294	1.5505
2.8	0.6738	2.8731	0.3149	0.2004	1.5711
3.0	0.6540	3.4245	0.2803	0.1765	1.5882

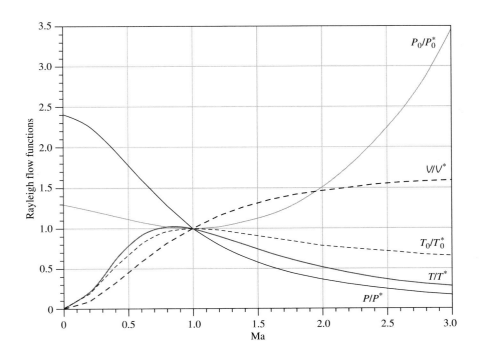

Appendix 2

PROPERTY TABLES AND CHARTS (ENGLISH UNITS)

TABLE A–1E

Molar mass, gas constant, and critical-point properties

Substance	Formula	Molar mass, M lbm/lbmol	Gas constant, R		Critical-point properties		
			Btu/ lbm $\cdot$ R*	psia $\cdot$ ft³/ lbm $\cdot$ R*	Temperature, R	Pressure, psia	Volume, ft³/lbmol
Air	—	28.97	0.06855	0.3704	238.5	547	1.41
Ammonia	NH_3	17.03	0.1166	0.6301	729.8	1636	1.16
Argon	Ar	39.948	0.04971	0.2686	272	705	1.20
Benzene	C_6H_6	78.115	0.02542	0.1374	1012	714	4.17
Bromine	Br_2	159.808	0.01243	0.06714	1052	1500	2.17
n-Butane	C_4H_{10}	58.124	0.03417	0.1846	765.2	551	4.08
Carbon dioxide	CO_2	44.01	0.04513	0.2438	547.5	1071	1.51
Carbon monoxide	CO	28.011	0.07090	0.3831	240	507	1.49
Carbon tetrachloride	CCl_4	153.82	0.01291	0.06976	1001.5	661	4.42
Chlorine	Cl_2	70.906	0.02801	0.1517	751	1120	1.99
Chloroform	$CHCl_3$	119.38	0.01664	0.08988	965.8	794	3.85
Dichlorodifluoromethane (R-12)	CCl_2F_2	120.91	0.01643	0.08874	692.4	582	3.49
Dichlorofluoromethane (R-21)	$CHCl_2F$	102.92	0.01930	0.1043	813.0	749	3.16
Ethane	C_2H_6	30.020	0.06616	0.3574	549.8	708	2.37
Ethyl alcohol	C_2H_5OH	46.07	0.04311	0.2329	929.0	926	2.68
Ethylene	C_2H_4	28.054	0.07079	0.3825	508.3	742	1.99
Helium	He	4.003	0.4961	2.6809	9.5	33.2	0.926
n-Hexane	C_6H_{14}	86.178	0.02305	0.1245	914.2	439	5.89
Hydrogen (normal)	H_2	2.016	0.9851	5.3224	59.9	188.1	1.04
Krypton	Kr	83.80	0.02370	0.1280	376.9	798	1.48
Methane	CH_4	16.043	0.1238	0.6688	343.9	673	1.59
Methyl alcohol	CH_3OH	32.042	0.06198	0.3349	923.7	1154	1.89
Methyl chloride	CH_3Cl	50.488	0.03934	0.2125	749.3	968	2.29
Neon	Ne	20.183	0.09840	0.5316	80.1	395	0.668
Nitrogen	N_2	28.013	0.07090	0.3830	227.1	492	1.44
Nitrous oxide	N_2O	44.013	0.04512	0.2438	557.4	1054	1.54
Oxygen	O_2	31.999	0.06206	0.3353	278.6	736	1.25
Propane	C_3H_8	44.097	0.04504	0.2433	665.9	617	3.20
Propylene	C_3H_6	42.081	0.04719	0.2550	656.9	670	2.90
Sulfur dioxide	SO_2	64.063	0.03100	1.1675	775.2	1143	1.95
Tetrafluoroethane (R-134a)	CF_3CH_2F	102.03	0.01946	0.1052	673.6	588.7	3.19
Trichlorofluoromethane (R-11)	CCl_3F	137.37	0.01446	0.07811	848.1	635	3.97
Water	H_2O	18.015	0.1102	0.5956	1164.8	3200	0.90
Xenon	Xe	131.30	0.01513	0.08172	521.55	852	1.90

*Calculated from $R = R_u/M$, where $R_u = 1.98588$ Btu/lbmol $\cdot$ R $= 10.7316$ psia $\cdot$ ft³/lbmol $\cdot$ R and M is the molar mass.

Source: K. A. Kobe and R. E. Lynn, Jr., Chemical Review 52 (1953), pp. 117–236, and ASHRAE, Handbook of Fundamentals (Atlanta, GA: American Society of Heating, Refrigerating, and Air-Conditioning Engineers, Inc., 1993), pp. 16.4 and 36.1.

TABLE A–2E

Ideal-gas specific heats of various common gases
(a) At 80°F

Gas	Formula	Gas constant, R Btu/lbm · R	c_p Btu/lbm · R	c_v Btu/lbm · R	k
Air	—	0.06855	0.240	0.171	1.400
Argon	Ar	0.04971	0.1253	0.0756	1.667
Butane	C_4H_{10}	0.03424	0.415	0.381	1.09
Carbon dioxide	CO_2	0.04513	0.203	0.158	1.285
Carbon monoxide	CO	0.07090	0.249	0.178	1.399
Ethane	C_2H_6	0.06616	0.427	0.361	1.183
Ethylene	C_2H_4	0.07079	0.411	0.340	1.208
Helium	He	0.4961	1.25	0.753	1.667
Hydrogen	H_2	0.9851	3.43	2.44	1.404
Methane	CH_4	0.1238	0.532	0.403	1.32
Neon	Ne	0.09840	0.246	0.1477	1.667
Nitrogen	N_2	0.07090	0.248	0.177	1.400
Octane	C_8H_{18}	0.01742	0.409	0.392	1.044
Oxygen	O_2	0.06206	0.219	0.157	1.395
Propane	C_3H_8	0.04504	0.407	0.362	1.124
Steam	H_2O	0.1102	0.445	0.335	1.329

Source: Gordon J. Van Wylen and Richard E. Sonntag, *Fundamentals of Classical Thermodynamics*, English/SI Version, 3rd ed. (New York: John Wiley & Sons, 1986), p. 687, Table A–8E.

(b) At various temperatures

Temp., °F	c_p Btu/lbm · R	c_v Btu/lbm · R	k	c_p Btu/lbm · R	c_v Btu/lbm · R	k	c_p Btu/lbm · R	c_v Btu/lbm · R	k
	Air			Carbon dioxide, CO_2			Carbon monoxide, CO		
40	0.240	0.171	1.401	0.195	0.150	1.300	0.248	0.177	1.400
100	0.240	0.172	1.400	0.205	0.160	1.283	0.249	0.178	1.399
200	0.241	0.173	1.397	0.217	0.172	1.262	0.249	0.179	1.397
300	0.243	0.174	1.394	0.229	0.184	1.246	0.251	0.180	1.394
400	0.245	0.176	1.389	0.239	0.193	1.233	0.253	0.182	1.389
500	0.248	0.179	1.383	0.247	0.202	1.223	0.256	0.185	1.384
600	0.250	0.182	1.377	0.255	0.210	1.215	0.259	0.188	1.377
700	0.254	0.185	1.371	0.262	0.217	1.208	0.262	0.191	1.371
800	0.257	0.188	1.365	0.269	0.224	1.202	0.266	0.195	1.364
900	0.259	0.191	1.358	0.275	0.230	1.197	0.269	0.198	1.357
1000	0.263	0.195	1.353	0.280	0.235	1.192	0.273	0.202	1.351
1500	0.276	0.208	1.330	0.298	0.253	1.178	0.287	0.216	1.328
2000	0.286	0.217	1.312	0.312	0.267	1.169	0.297	0.226	1.314
	Hydrogen, H_2			Nitrogen, N_2			Oxygen, O_2		
40	3.397	2.412	1.409	0.248	0.177	1.400	0.219	0.156	1.397
100	3.426	2.441	1.404	0.248	0.178	1.399	0.220	0.158	1.394
200	3.451	2.466	1.399	0.249	0.178	1.398	0.223	0.161	1.387
300	3.461	2.476	1.398	0.250	0.179	1.396	0.226	0.164	1.378
400	3.466	2.480	1.397	0.251	0.180	1.393	0.230	0.168	1.368
500	3.469	2.484	1.397	0.254	0.183	1.388	0.235	0.173	1.360
600	3.473	2.488	1.396	0.256	0.185	1.383	0.239	0.177	1.352
700	3.477	2.492	1.395	0.260	0.189	1.377	0.242	0.181	1.344
800	3.494	2.509	1.393	0.262	0.191	1.371	0.246	0.184	1.337
900	3.502	2.519	1.392	0.265	0.194	1.364	0.249	0.187	1.331
1000	3.513	2.528	1.390	0.269	0.198	1.359	0.252	0.190	1.326
1500	3.618	2.633	1.374	0.283	0.212	1.334	0.263	0.201	1.309
2000	3.758	2.773	1.355	0.293	0.222	1.319	0.270	0.208	1.298

Note: The unit Btu/lbm · R is equivalent to Btu/lbm · °F.

Source: Kenneth Wark, *Thermodynamics*, 4th ed. (New York: McGraw-Hill, 1983), p. 830, Table A–4. Originally published in *Tables of Properties of Gases*, NBS Circular 564, 1955.

Ideal-gas specific heats of various common gases (*Concluded*)
(*c*) As a function of temperature

$$\bar{c}_p = a + bT + cT^2 + dT^3$$
(*T* in R, c_p in Btu/lbmol · R)

Substance	Formula	a	b	c	d	Temperature range, R	% error Max.	% error Avg.
Nitrogen	N_2	6.903	-0.02085×10^{-2}	0.05957×10^{-5}	-0.1176×10^{-9}	491-3240	0.59	0.34
Oxygen	O_2	6.085	0.2017×10^{-2}	-0.05275×10^{-5}	0.05372×10^{-9}	491-3240	1.19	0.28
Air	—	6.713	0.02609×10^{-2}	0.03540×10^{-5}	-0.08052×10^{-9}	491-3240	0.72	0.33
Hydrogen	H_2	6.952	-0.02542×10^{-2}	0.02952×10^{-5}	-0.03565×10^{-9}	491-3240	1.02	0.26
Carbon monoxide	CO	6.726	0.02222×10^{-2}	0.03960×10^{-5}	-0.09100×10^{-9}	491-3240	0.89	0.37
Carbon dioxide	CO_2	5.316	0.79361×10^{-2}	-0.2581×10^{-5}	0.3059×10^{-9}	491-3240	0.67	0.22
Water vapor	H_2O	7.700	0.02552×10^{-2}	0.07781×10^{-5}	-0.1472×10^{-9}	491-3240	0.53	0.24
Nitric oxide	NO	7.008	-0.01247×10^{-2}	0.07185×10^{-5}	-0.1715×10^{-9}	491-2700	0.97	0.36
Nitrous oxide	N_2O	5.758	0.7780×10^{-2}	-0.2596×10^{-5}	0.4331×10^{-9}	491-2700	0.59	0.26
Nitrogen dioxide	NO_2	5.48	0.7583×10^{-2}	-0.260×10^{-5}	0.322×10^{-9}	491-2700	0.46	0.18
Ammonia	NH_3	6.5846	0.34028×10^{-2}	0.073034×10^{-5}	-0.27402×10^{-9}	491-2700	0.91	0.36
Sulfur	S_2	6.499	0.2943×10^{-2}	-0.1200×10^{-5}	0.1632×10^{-9}	491-3240	0.99	0.38
Sulfur dioxide	SO_2	6.157	0.7689×10^{-2}	-0.2810×10^{-5}	0.3527×10^{-9}	491-3240	0.45	0.24
Sulfur trioxide	SO_3	3.918	1.935×10^{-2}	-0.8256×10^{-5}	1.328×10^{-9}	491-2340	0.29	0.13
Acetylene	C_2H_2	5.21	1.2227×10^{-2}	-0.4812×10^{-5}	0.7457×10^{-9}	491-2700	1.46	0.59
Benzene	C_6H_6	-8.650	6.4322×10^{-2}	-2.327×10^{-5}	3.179×10^{-9}	491-2700	0.34	0.20
Methanol	CH_4O	4.55	1.214×10^{-2}	-0.0898×10^{-5}	-0.329×10^{-9}	491-1800	0.18	0.08
Ethanol	C_2H_6O	4.75	2.781×10^{-2}	-0.7651×10^{-5}	0.821×10^{-9}	491-2700	0.40	0.22
Hydrogen chloride	HCl	7.244	-0.1011×10^{-2}	0.09783×10^{-5}	-0.1776×10^{-9}	491-2740	0.22	0.08
Methane	CH_4	4.750	0.6666×10^{-2}	0.09352×10^{-5}	-0.4510×10^{-9}	491-2740	1.33	0.57
Ethane	C_2H_6	1.648	2.291×10^{-2}	-0.4722×10^{-5}	0.2984×10^{-9}	491-2740	0.83	0.28
Propane	C_3H_8	-0.966	4.044×10^{-2}	-1.159×10^{-5}	1.300×10^{-9}	491-2740	0.40	0.12
n-Butane	C_4H_{10}	0.945	4.929×10^{-2}	-1.352×10^{-5}	1.433×10^{-9}	491-2740	0.54	0.24
i-Butane	C_4H_{10}	-1.890	5.520×10^{-2}	-1.696×10^{-5}	2.044×10^{-9}	491-2740	0.25	0.13
n-Pentane	C_5H_{12}	1.618	6.028×10^{-2}	-1.656×10^{-5}	1.732×10^{-9}	491-2740	0.56	0.21
n-Hexane	C_6H_{14}	1.657	7.328×10^{-2}	-2.112×10^{-5}	2.363×10^{-9}	491-2740	0.72	0.20
Ethylene	C_2H_4	0.944	2.075×10^{-2}	-0.6151×10^{-5}	0.7326×10^{-9}	491-2740	0.54	0.13
Propylene	C_3H_6	0.753	3.162×10^{-2}	-0.8981×10^{-5}	1.008×10^{-9}	491-2740	0.73	0.17

Source: Chemical and Process Thermodynamics 3/E by Kyle, B. G., © 2000. Adapted by permission of Pearson Education, Inc., Upper Saddle River, NJ.

Properties of common liquids, solids, and foods
(*a*) Liquids

Substance	Boiling data at 1 atm		Freezing data		Liquid properties		
	Normal boiling point, °F	Latent heat of vaporization, h_{fg} Btu/lbm	Freezing point, °F	Latent heat of fusion, h_{if} Btu/lbm	Temperature, °F	Density, ρ lbm/ft^3	Specific heat, c_p Btu/lbm · R
Ammonia	−27.9	24.54	−107.9	138.6	−27.9	42.6	1.06
					0	41.3	1.083
					40	39.5	1.103
					80	37.5	1.135
Argon	−302.6	69.5	−308.7	12.0	−302.6	87.0	0.272
Benzene	176.4	169.4	41.9	54.2	68	54.9	0.411
Brine (20% sodium chloride by mass)	219.0	—	0.7	—	68	71.8	0.743
n-Butane	31.1	165.6	−217.3	34.5	31.1	37.5	0.552
Carbon dioxide	−109.2*	99.6 (at 32°F)	−69.8	—	32	57.8	0.583
Ethanol	172.8	360.5	−173.6	46.9	77	48.9	0.588
Ethyl alcohol	173.5	368	−248.8	46.4	68	49.3	0.678
Ethylene glycol	388.6	344.0	12.6	77.9	68	69.2	0.678
Glycerine	355.8	419	66.0	86.3	68	78.7	0.554
Helium	−452.1	9.80	—	—	−452.1	9.13	5.45
Hydrogen	−423.0	191.7	−434.5	25.6	−423.0	4.41	2.39
Isobutane	10.9	157.8	−255.5	45.5	10.9	37.1	0.545
Kerosene	399–559	108	−12.8	—	68	51.2	0.478
Mercury	674.1	126.7	−38.0	4.90	77	847	0.033
Methane	−258.7	219.6	296.0	25.1	−258.7	26.4	0.834
					−160	20.0	1.074
Methanol	148.1	473	−143.9	42.7	77	49.1	0.609
Nitrogen	−320.4	85.4	−346.0	10.9	−320.4	50.5	0.492
					−260	38.2	0.643
Octane	256.6	131.7	−71.5	77.9	68	43.9	0.502
Oil (light)	—	—			77	56.8	0.430
Oxygen	−297.3	91.5	−361.8	5.9	−297.3	71.2	0.408
Petroleum	—	99–165			68	40.0	0.478
Propane	−43.7	184.0	−305.8	34.4	−43.7	36.3	0.538
					32	33.0	0.604
					100	29.4	0.673
Refrigerant-134a	−15.0	93.3	−141.9	—	−40	88.5	0.283
					−15	86.0	0.294
					32	80.9	0.318
					90	73.6	0.348
Water	212	970.1	32	143.5	32	62.4	1.01
					90	62.1	1.00
					150	61.2	1.00
					212	59.8	1.01

*Sublimation temperature. (At pressures below the triple-point pressure of 75.1 psia, carbon dioxide exists as a solid or gas. Also, the freezing-point temperature of carbon dioxide is the triple-point temperature of −69.8°F.)

TABLE A–3E

Properties of common liquids, solids, and foods (*Continued*)

(*b*) Solids (values are for room temperature unless indicated otherwise)

Substance	Density, ρ lbm/ft^3	Specific heat, c_p Btu/lbm · R	Substance	Density, ρ lbm/ft^3	Specific heat, c_p Btu/lbm · R
Metals			**Nonmetals**		
Aluminum			Asphalt	132	0.220
−100°F		0.192	Brick, common	120	0.189
32°F		0.212	Brick, fireclay (500°C)	144	0.229
100°F	170	0.218	Concrete	144	0.156
200°F		0.224	Clay	62.4	0.220
300°F		0.229	Diamond	151	0.147
400°F		0.235	Glass, window	169	0.191
500°F		0.240	Glass, pyrex	139	0.200
Bronze (76% Cu, 2% Zn, 2% Al)	517	0.0955	Graphite	156	0.170
Brass, yellow (65% Cu, 35% Zn)	519	0.0955	Granite	169	0.243
			Gypsum or plaster board	50	0.260
Copper			Ice		
−60°F		0.0862	−50°F		0.424
0°F		0.0893	0°F		0.471
100°F	555	0.0925	20°F		0.491
200°F		0.0938	32°F	57.5	0.502
390°F		0.0963	Limestone	103	0.217
Iron	490	0.107	Marble	162	0.210
Lead	705	0.030	Plywood (Douglas fir)	34.0	
Magnesium	108	0.239	Rubber (soft)	68.7	
Nickel	555	0.105	Rubber (hard)	71.8	
Silver	655	0.056	Sand	94.9	
Steel, mild	489	0.119	Stone	93.6	
Tungsten	1211	0.031	Woods, hard (maple, oak, etc.)	45.0	
			Woods, soft (fir, pine, etc.)	32.0	

(*c*) Foods

Food	Water content, % (mass)	Freezing point, °F	Specific heat, Btu/lbm · R Above freezing	Specific heat, Btu/lbm · R Below freezing	Latent heat of fusion, Btu/lbm	Food	Water content, % (mass)	Freezing point, °F	Specific heat, Btu/lbm · R Above freezing	Specific heat, Btu/lbm · R Below freezing	Latent heat of fusion, Btu/lbm
Apples	84	30	0.873	0.453	121	Lettuce	95	32	0.961	0.487	136
Bananas	75	31	0.801	0.426	108	Milk, whole	88	31	0.905	0.465	126
Beef round	67	—	0.737	0.402	96	Oranges	87	31	0.897	0.462	125
Broccoli	90	31	0.921	0.471	129	Potatoes	78	31	0.825	0.435	112
Butter	16	—	—	0.249	23	Salmon fish	64	28	0.713	0.393	92
Cheese, Swiss	39	14	0.513	0.318	56	Shrimp	83	28	0.865	0.450	119
Cherries	80	29	0.841	0.441	115	Spinach	93	31	0.945	0.481	134
Chicken	74	27	0.793	0.423	106	Strawberries	90	31	0.921	0.471	129
Corn, sweet	74	31	0.793	0.423	106	Tomatoes, ripe	94	31	0.953	0.484	135
Eggs, whole	74	31	0.793	0.423	106	Turkey	64	—	0.713	0.393	92
Ice cream	63	22	0.705	0.390	90	Watermelon	93	31	0.945	0.481	134

Source: Values are obtained from various handbooks and other sources or are calculated. Water content and freezing-point data of foods are from ASHRAE, *Handbook of Fundamentals*, I-P version (Atlanta, GA: American Society of Heating, Refrigerating, and Air-Conditioning Engineers, Inc., 1993), Chap. 30, Table 1. Freezing point is the temperature at which freezing starts for fruits and vegetables, and the average freezing temperature for other foods.

TABLE A–4E

Saturated water—Temperature table

Temp., T °F	Sat. press., P_{sat} psia	Specific volume, ft³/lbm		Internal energy, Btu/lbm			Enthalpy, Btu/lbm			Entropy, Btu/lbm · R		
		Sat. liquid, v_f	Sat. vapor, v_g	Sat. liquid, u_f	Evap., u_{fg}	Sat. vapor, u_g	Sat. liquid, h_f	Evap., h_{fg}	Sat. vapor, h_g	Sat. liquid, s_f	Evap., s_{fg}	Sat. vapor, s_g
32.018	0.08871	0.01602	3299.9	0.000	1021.0	1021.0	0.000	1075.2	1075.2	0.00000	2.18672	2.1867
35	0.09998	0.01602	2945.7	3.004	1019.0	1022.0	3.004	1073.5	1076.5	0.00609	2.17011	2.1762
40	0.12173	0.01602	2443.6	8.032	1015.6	1023.7	8.032	1070.7	1078.7	0.01620	2.14271	2.1589
45	0.14756	0.01602	2035.8	13.05	1012.2	1025.3	13.05	1067.8	1080.9	0.02620	2.11587	2.1421
50	0.17812	0.01602	1703.1	18.07	1008.9	1026.9	18.07	1065.0	1083.1	0.03609	2.08956	2.1256
55	0.21413	0.01603	1430.4	23.07	1005.5	1028.6	23.07	1062.2	1085.3	0.04586	2.06377	2.1096
60	0.25638	0.01604	1206.1	28.08	1002.1	1030.2	28.08	1059.4	1087.4	0.05554	2.03847	2.0940
65	0.30578	0.01604	1020.8	33.08	998.76	1031.8	33.08	1056.5	1089.6	0.06511	2.01366	2.0788
70	0.36334	0.01605	867.18	38.08	995.39	1033.5	38.08	1053.7	1091.8	0.07459	1.98931	2.0639
75	0.43016	0.01606	739.27	43.07	992.02	1035.1	43.07	1050.9	1093.9	0.08398	1.96541	2.0494
80	0.50745	0.01607	632.41	48.06	988.65	1036.7	48.07	1048.0	1096.1	0.09328	1.94196	2.0352
85	0.59659	0.01609	542.80	53.06	985.28	1038.3	53.06	1045.2	1098.3	0.10248	1.91892	2.0214
90	0.69904	0.01610	467.40	58.05	981.90	1040.0	58.05	1042.4	1100.4	0.11161	1.89630	2.0079
95	0.81643	0.01612	403.74	63.04	978.52	1041.6	63.04	1039.5	1102.6	0.12065	1.87408	1.9947
100	0.95052	0.01613	349.83	68.03	975.14	1043.2	68.03	1036.7	1104.7	0.12961	1.85225	1.9819
110	1.2767	0.01617	264.96	78.01	968.36	1046.4	78.02	1031.0	1109.0	0.14728	1.80970	1.9570
120	1.6951	0.01620	202.94	88.00	961.56	1049.6	88.00	1025.2	1113.2	0.16466	1.76856	1.9332
130	2.2260	0.01625	157.09	97.99	954.73	1052.7	97.99	1019.4	1117.4	0.18174	1.72877	1.9105
140	2.8931	0.01629	122.81	107.98	947.87	1055.9	107.99	1013.6	1121.6	0.19855	1.69024	1.8888
150	3.7234	0.01634	96.929	117.98	940.98	1059.0	117.99	1007.8	1125.7	0.21508	1.65291	1.8680
160	4.7474	0.01639	77.185	127.98	934.05	1062.0	128.00	1001.8	1129.8	0.23136	1.61670	1.8481
170	5.9999	0.01645	61.982	138.00	927.08	1065.1	138.02	995.88	1133.9	0.24739	1.58155	1.8289
180	7.5197	0.01651	50.172	148.02	920.06	1068.1	148.04	989.85	1137.9	0.26318	1.54741	1.8106
190	9.3497	0.01657	40.920	158.05	912.99	1071.0	158.08	983.76	1141.8	0.27874	1.51421	1.7930
200	11.538	0.01663	33.613	168.10	905.87	1074.0	168.13	977.60	1145.7	0.29409	1.48191	1.7760
210	14.136	0.01670	27.798	178.15	898.68	1076.8	178.20	971.35	1149.5	0.30922	1.45046	1.7597
212	14.709	0.01671	26.782	180.16	897.24	1077.4	180.21	970.09	1150.3	0.31222	1.44427	1.7565
220	17.201	0.01677	23.136	188.22	891.43	1079.6	188.28	965.02	1153.3	0.32414	1.41980	1.7439
230	20.795	0.01684	19.374	198.31	884.10	1082.4	198.37	958.59	1157.0	0.33887	1.38989	1.7288
240	24.985	0.01692	16.316	208.41	876.70	1085.1	208.49	952.06	1160.5	0.35342	1.36069	1.7141
250	29.844	0.01700	13.816	218.54	869.21	1087.7	218.63	945.41	1164.0	0.36779	1.33216	1.6999
260	35.447	0.01708	11.760	228.68	861.62	1090.3	228.79	938.65	1167.4	0.38198	1.30425	1.6862
270	41.877	0.01717	10.059	238.85	853.94	1092.8	238.98	931.76	1170.7	0.39601	1.27694	1.6730
280	49.222	0.01726	8.6439	249.04	846.16	1095.2	249.20	924.74	1173.9	0.40989	1.25018	1.6601
290	57.573	0.01735	7.4607	259.26	838.27	1097.5	259.45	917.57	1177.0	0.42361	1.22393	1.6475
300	67.028	0.01745	6.4663	269.51	830.25	1099.8	269.73	910.24	1180.0	0.43720	1.19818	1.6354
310	77.691	0.01755	5.6266	279.79	822.11	1101.9	280.05	902.75	1182.8	0.45065	1.17289	1.6235
320	89.667	0.01765	4.9144	290.11	813.84	1104.0	290.40	895.09	1185.5	0.46396	1.14802	1.6120
330	103.07	0.01776	4.3076	300.46	805.43	1105.9	300.80	887.25	1188.1	0.47716	1.12355	1.6007
340	118.02	0.01787	3.7885	310.85	796.87	1107.7	311.24	879.22	1190.5	0.49024	1.09945	1.5897
350	134.63	0.01799	3.3425	321.29	788.16	1109.4	321.73	870.98	1192.7	0.50321	1.07570	1.5789
360	153.03	0.01811	2.9580	331.76	779.28	1111.0	332.28	862.53	1194.8	0.51607	1.05227	1.5683
370	173.36	0.01823	2.6252	342.29	770.23	1112.5	342.88	853.86	1196.7	0.52884	1.02914	1.5580
380	195.74	0.01836	2.3361	352.87	761.00	1113.9	353.53	844.96	1198.5	0.54152	1.00628	1.5478
390	220.33	0.01850	2.0842	363.50	751.58	1115.1	364.25	835.81	1200.1	0.55411	0.98366	1.5378

TABLE A–4E

Saturated water—Temperature table (*Concluded*)

Temp., T °F	Sat. press., P_{sat} psia	Specific volume, ft³/lbm		Internal energy, Btu/lbm			Enthalpy, Btu/lbm			Entropy, Btu/lbm · R		
		Sat. liquid, v_f	Sat. vapor, v_g	Sat. liquid, u_f	Evap., u_{fg}	Sat. vapor, u_g	Sat. liquid, h_f	Evap., h_{fg}	Sat. vapor, h_g	Sat. liquid, s_f	Evap., s_{fg}	Sat. vapor, s_g
400	247.26	0.01864	1.8639	374.19	741.97	1116.2	375.04	826.39	1201.4	0.56663	0.96127	1.5279
410	276.69	0.01878	1.6706	384.94	732.14	1117.1	385.90	816.71	1202.6	0.57907	0.93908	1.5182
420	308.76	0.01894	1.5006	395.76	722.08	1117.8	396.84	806.74	1203.6	0.59145	0.91707	1.5085
430	343.64	0.01910	1.3505	406.65	711.80	1118.4	407.86	796.46	1204.3	0.60377	0.89522	1.4990
440	381.49	0.01926	1.2178	417.61	701.26	1118.9	418.97	785.87	1204.8	0.61603	0.87349	1.4895
450	422.47	0.01944	1.0999	428.66	690.47	1119.1	430.18	774.94	1205.1	0.62826	0.85187	1.4801
460	466.75	0.01962	0.99510	439.79	679.39	1119.2	441.48	763.65	1205.1	0.64044	0.83033	1.4708
470	514.52	0.01981	0.90158	451.01	668.02	1119.0	452.90	751.98	1204.9	0.65260	0.80885	1.4615
480	565.96	0.02001	0.81794	462.34	656.34	1118.7	464.43	739.91	1204.3	0.66474	0.78739	1.4521
490	621.24	0.02022	0.74296	473.77	644.32	1118.1	476.09	727.40	1203.5	0.67686	0.76594	1.4428
500	680.56	0.02044	0.67558	485.32	631.94	1117.3	487.89	714.44	1202.3	0.68899	0.74445	1.4334
510	744.11	0.02067	0.61489	496.99	619.17	1116.2	499.84	700.99	1200.8	0.70112	0.72290	1.4240
520	812.11	0.02092	0.56009	508.80	605.99	1114.8	511.94	687.01	1199.0	0.71327	0.70126	1.4145
530	884.74	0.02118	0.51051	520.76	592.35	1113.1	524.23	672.47	1196.7	0.72546	0.67947	1.4049
540	962.24	0.02146	0.46553	532.88	578.23	1111.1	536.70	657.31	1194.0	0.73770	0.65751	1.3952
550	1044.8	0.02176	0.42465	545.18	563.58	1108.8	549.39	641.47	1190.9	0.75000	0.63532	1.3853
560	1132.7	0.02207	0.38740	557.68	548.33	1106.0	562.31	624.91	1187.2	0.76238	0.61284	1.3752
570	1226.2	0.02242	0.35339	570.40	532.45	1102.8	575.49	607.55	1183.0	0.77486	0.59003	1.3649
580	1325.5	0.02279	0.32225	583.37	515.84	1099.2	588.95	589.29	1178.2	0.78748	0.56679	1.3543
590	1430.8	0.02319	0.29367	596.61	498.43	1095.0	602.75	570.04	1172.8	0.80026	0.54306	1.3433
600	1542.5	0.02362	0.26737	610.18	480.10	1090.3	616.92	549.67	1166.6	0.81323	0.51871	1.3319
610	1660.9	0.02411	0.24309	624.11	460.73	1084.8	631.52	528.03	1159.5	0.82645	0.49363	1.3201
620	1786.2	0.02464	0.22061	638.47	440.14	1078.6	646.62	504.92	1151.5	0.83998	0.46765	1.3076
630	1918.9	0.02524	0.19972	653.35	418.12	1071.5	662.32	480.07	1142.4	0.85389	0.44056	1.2944
640	2059.3	0.02593	0.18019	668.86	394.36	1063.2	678.74	453.14	1131.9	0.86828	0.41206	1.2803
650	2207.8	0.02673	0.16184	685.16	368.44	1053.6	696.08	423.65	1119.7	0.88332	0.38177	1.2651
660	2364.9	0.02767	0.14444	702.48	339.74	1042.2	714.59	390.84	1105.4	0.89922	0.34906	1.2483
670	2531.2	0.02884	0.12774	721.23	307.22	1028.5	734.74	353.54	1088.3	0.91636	0.31296	1.2293
680	2707.3	0.03035	0.11134	742.11	269.00	1011.1	757.32	309.57	1066.9	0.93541	0.27163	1.2070
690	2894.1	0.03255	0.09451	766.81	220.77	987.6	784.24	253.96	1038.2	0.95797	0.22089	1.1789
700	3093.0	0.03670	0.07482	801.75	146.50	948.3	822.76	168.32	991.1	0.99023	0.14514	1.1354
705.10	3200.1	0.04975	0.04975	866.61	0	866.6	896.07	0	896.1	1.05257	0	1.0526

Source: Tables A–4E through A–8E are generated using the Engineering Equation Solver (EES) software developed by S. A. Klein and F. L. Alvarado. The routine used in calculations is the highly accurate Steam_IAPWS, which incorporates the 1995 Formulation for the Thermodynamic Properties of Ordinary Water Substance for General and Scientific Use, issued by The International Association for the Properties of Water and Steam (IAPWS). This formulation replaces the 1984 formulation of Haar, Gallagher, and Kell (NBS/NRC Steam Tables, Hemisphere Publishing Co., 1984), which is also available in EES as the routine STEAM. The new formulation is based on the correlations of Saul and Wagner (J. Phys. Chem. Ref. Data, 16, 893, 1987) with modifications to adjust to the International Temperature Scale of 1990. The modifications are described by Wagner and Pruss (J. Phys. Chem. Ref. Data, 22, 783, 1993). The properties of ice are based on Hyland and Wexler, "Formulations for the Thermodynamic Properties of the Saturated Phases of H₂O from 173.15 K to 473.15 K," ASHRAE Trans., Part 2A, Paper 2793, 1983.

TABLE A–5E

Saturated water—Pressure table

Press., P psia	Sat. temp., T_{sat} °F	Specific volume, ft³/lbm Sat. liquid, v_f	Sat. vapor, v_g	Internal energy, Btu/lbm Sat. liquid, u_f	Evap., u_{fg}	Sat. vapor, u_g	Enthalpy, Btu/lbm Sat. liquid, h_f	Evap., h_{fg}	Sat. vapor, h_g	Entropy, Btu/lbm · R Sat. liquid, s_f	Evap., s_{fg}	Sat. vapor, s_g
1	101.69	0.01614	333.49	69.72	973.99	1043.7	69.72	1035.7	1105.4	0.13262	1.84495	1.9776
2	126.02	0.01623	173.71	94.02	957.45	1051.5	94.02	1021.7	1115.8	0.17499	1.74444	1.9194
3	141.41	0.01630	118.70	109.39	946.90	1056.3	109.40	1012.8	1122.2	0.20090	1.68489	1.8858
4	152.91	0.01636	90.629	120.89	938.97	1059.9	120.90	1006.0	1126.9	0.21985	1.64225	1.8621
5	162.18	0.01641	73.525	130.17	932.53	1062.7	130.18	1000.5	1130.7	0.23488	1.60894	1.8438
6	170.00	0.01645	61.982	138.00	927.08	1065.1	138.02	995.88	1133.9	0.24739	1.58155	1.8289
8	182.81	0.01652	47.347	150.83	918.08	1068.9	150.86	988.15	1139.0	0.26757	1.53800	1.8056
10	193.16	0.01659	38.425	161.22	910.75	1072.0	161.25	981.82	1143.1	0.28362	1.50391	1.7875
14.696	211.95	0.01671	26.805	180.12	897.27	1077.4	180.16	970.12	1150.3	0.31215	1.44441	1.7566
15	212.99	0.01672	26.297	181.16	896.52	1077.7	181.21	969.47	1150.7	0.31370	1.44441	1.7549
20	227.92	0.01683	20.093	196.21	885.63	1081.8	196.27	959.93	1156.2	0.33582	1.39606	1.7319
25	240.03	0.01692	16.307	208.45	876.67	1085.1	208.52	952.03	1160.6	0.35347	1.36060	1.7141
30	250.30	0.01700	13.749	218.84	868.98	1087.8	218.93	945.21	1164.1	0.36821	1.33132	1.6995
35	259.25	0.01708	11.901	227.92	862.19	1090.1	228.03	939.16	1167.2	0.38093	1.30632	1.6872
40	267.22	0.01715	10.501	236.02	856.09	1092.1	236.14	933.69	1169.8	0.39213	1.28448	1.6766
45	274.41	0.01721	9.4028	243.34	850.52	1093.9	243.49	928.68	1172.2	0.40216	1.26506	1.6672
50	280.99	0.01727	8.5175	250.05	845.39	1095.4	250.21	924.03	1174.2	0.41125	1.24756	1.6588
55	287.05	0.01732	7.7882	256.25	840.61	1096.9	256.42	919.70	1176.1	0.41958	1.23162	1.6512
60	292.69	0.01738	7.1766	262.01	836.13	1098.1	262.20	915.61	1177.8	0.42728	1.21697	1.6442
65	297.95	0.01743	6.6560	267.41	831.90	1099.3	267.62	911.75	1179.4	0.43443	1.20341	1.6378
70	302.91	0.01748	6.2075	272.50	827.90	1100.4	272.72	908.08	1180.8	0.44112	1.19078	1.6319
75	307.59	0.01752	5.8167	277.31	824.09	1101.4	277.55	904.58	1182.1	0.44741	1.17895	1.6264
80	312.02	0.01757	5.4733	281.87	820.45	1102.3	282.13	901.22	1183.4	0.45335	1.16783	1.6212
85	316.24	0.01761	5.1689	286.22	816.97	1103.2	286.50	898.00	1184.5	0.45897	1.15732	1.6163
90	320.26	0.01765	4.8972	290.38	813.62	1104.0	290.67	894.89	1185.6	0.46431	1.14737	1.6117
95	324.11	0.01770	4.6532	294.36	810.40	1104.8	294.67	891.89	1186.6	0.46941	1.13791	1.6073
100	327.81	0.01774	4.4327	298.19	807.29	1105.5	298.51	888.99	1187.5	0.47427	1.12888	1.6032
110	334.77	0.01781	4.0410	305.41	801.37	1106.8	305.78	883.44	1189.2	0.48341	1.11201	1.5954
120	341.25	0.01789	3.7289	312.16	795.79	1107.9	312.55	878.20	1190.8	0.49187	1.09646	1.5883
130	347.32	0.01796	3.4557	318.48	790.51	1109.0	318.92	873.21	1192.1	0.49974	1.08204	1.5818
140	353.03	0.01802	3.2202	324.45	785.49	1109.9	324.92	868.45	1193.4	0.50711	1.06858	1.5757
150	358.42	0.01809	3.0150	330.11	780.69	1110.8	330.61	863.88	1194.5	0.51405	1.05595	1.5700
160	363.54	0.01815	2.8347	335.49	776.10	1111.6	336.02	859.49	1195.5	0.52061	1.04405	1.5647
170	368.41	0.01821	2.6749	340.62	771.68	1112.3	341.19	855.25	1196.4	0.52682	1.03279	1.5596
180	373.07	0.01827	2.5322	345.53	767.42	1113.0	346.14	851.16	1197.3	0.53274	1.02210	1.5548
190	377.52	0.01833	2.4040	350.24	763.31	1113.6	350.89	847.19	1198.1	0.53839	1.01191	1.5503
200	381.80	0.01839	2.2882	354.78	759.32	1114.1	355.46	843.33	1198.8	0.54379	1.00219	1.5460
250	400.97	0.01865	1.8440	375.23	741.02	1116.3	376.09	825.47	1201.6	0.56784	0.95912	1.5270
300	417.35	0.01890	1.5435	392.89	724.77	1117.7	393.94	809.41	1203.3	0.58818	0.92289	1.5111
350	431.74	0.01912	1.3263	408.55	709.98	1118.5	409.79	794.65	1204.4	0.60590	0.89143	1.4973
400	444.62	0.01934	1.1617	422.70	696.31	1119.0	424.13	780.87	1205.0	0.62168	0.86350	1.4852
450	456.31	0.01955	1.0324	435.67	683.52	1119.2	437.30	767.86	1205.2	0.63595	0.83828	1.4742
500	467.04	0.01975	0.92819	447.68	671.42	1119.1	449.51	755.48	1205.0	0.64900	0.81521	1.4642
550	476.97	0.01995	0.84228	458.90	659.91	1118.8	460.93	743.60	1204.5	0.66107	0.79388	1.4550
600	486.24	0.02014	0.77020	469.46	648.88	1118.3	471.70	732.15	1203.9	0.67231	0.77400	1.4463

TABLE A–5E

Saturated water—Pressure table (*Concluded*)

H₂O

Press., P psia	Sat. temp., T_{sat} °F	Specific volume, ft³/lbm		Internal energy, Btu/lbm			Enthalpy, Btu/lbm			Entropy, Btu/lbm · R		
		Sat. liquid, v_f	Sat. vapor, v_g	Sat. liquid, u_f	Evap., u_{fg}	Sat. vapor, u_g	Sat. liquid, h_f	Evap., h_{fg}	Sat. vapor, h_g	Sat. liquid, s_f	Evap., s_{fg}	Sat. vapor, s_g
700	503.13	0.02051	0.65589	488.96	627.98	1116.9	491.62	710.29	1201.9	0.69279	0.73771	1.4305
800	518.27	0.02087	0.56920	506.74	608.30	1115.0	509.83	689.48	1199.3	0.71117	0.70502	1.4162
900	532.02	0.02124	0.50107	523.19	589.54	1112.7	526.73	669.46	1196.2	0.72793	0.67505	1.4030
1000	544.65	0.02159	0.44604	538.58	571.49	1110.1	542.57	650.03	1192.6	0.74341	0.64722	1.3906
1200	567.26	0.02232	0.36241	566.89	536.87	1103.8	571.85	612.39	1184.2	0.77143	0.59632	1.3677
1400	587.14	0.02307	0.30161	592.79	503.50	1096.3	598.76	575.66	1174.4	0.79658	0.54991	1.3465
1600	604.93	0.02386	0.25516	616.99	470.69	1087.7	624.06	539.18	1163.2	0.81972	0.50645	1.3262
1800	621.07	0.02470	0.21831	640.03	437.86	1077.9	648.26	502.35	1150.6	0.84144	0.46482	1.3063
2000	635.85	0.02563	0.18815	662.33	404.46	1066.8	671.82	464.60	1136.4	0.86224	0.42409	1.2863
2500	668.17	0.02860	0.13076	717.67	313.53	1031.2	730.90	360.79	1091.7	0.91311	0.31988	1.2330
3000	695.41	0.03433	0.08460	783.39	186.41	969.8	802.45	214.32	1016.8	0.97321	0.18554	1.1587
3200.1	705.10	0.04975	0.04975	866.61	0	866.6	896.07	0	896.1	1.05257	0	1.0526

Superheated water

T °F	v ft³/lbm	u Btu/lbm	h Btu/lbm	s Btu/lbm·R	v ft³/lbm	u Btu/lbm	h Btu/lbm	s Btu/lbm·R	v ft³/lbm	u Btu/lbm	h Btu/lbm	s Btu/lbm·R
	P = 1.0 psia (101.69°F)*				P = 5.0 psia (162.18°F)				P = 10 psia (193.16°F)			
Sat.†	333.49	1043.7	1105.4	1.9776	73.525	1062.7	1130.7	1.8438	38.425	1072.0	1143.1	1.7875
200	392.53	1077.5	1150.1	2.0509	78.153	1076.2	1148.5	1.8716	38.849	1074.5	1146.4	1.7926
240	416.44	1091.2	1168.3	2.0777	83.009	1090.3	1167.1	1.8989	41.326	1089.1	1165.5	1.8207
280	440.33	1105.0	1186.5	2.1030	87.838	1104.3	1185.6	1.9246	43.774	1103.4	1184.4	1.8469
320	464.20	1118.9	1204.8	2.1271	92.650	1118.4	1204.1	1.9490	46.205	1117.6	1203.1	1.8716
360	488.07	1132.9	1223.3	2.1502	97.452	1132.5	1222.6	1.9722	48.624	1131.9	1221.8	1.8950
400	511.92	1147.1	1241.8	2.1722	102.25	1146.7	1241.3	1.9944	51.035	1146.2	1240.6	1.9174
440	535.77	1161.3	1260.4	2.1934	107.03	1160.9	1260.0	2.0156	53.441	1160.5	1259.4	1.9388
500	571.54	1182.8	1288.6	2.2237	114.21	1182.6	1288.2	2.0461	57.041	1182.2	1287.8	1.9693
600	631.14	1219.4	1336.2	2.2709	126.15	1219.2	1335.9	2.0933	63.029	1219.0	1335.6	2.0167
700	690.73	1256.8	1384.6	2.3146	138.09	1256.7	1384.4	2.1371	69.007	1256.5	1384.2	2.0605
800	750.31	1295.1	1433.9	2.3553	150.02	1294.9	1433.7	2.1778	74.980	1294.8	1433.5	2.1013
1000	869.47	1374.2	1535.1	2.4299	173.86	1374.2	1535.0	2.2524	86.913	1374.1	1534.9	2.1760
1200	988.62	1457.1	1640.0	2.4972	197.70	1457.0	1640.0	2.3198	98.840	1457.0	1639.9	2.2433
1400	1107.8	1543.7	1748.7	2.5590	221.54	1543.7	1748.7	2.3816	110.762	1543.6	1748.6	2.3052
	P = 15 psia (212.99°F)				P = 20 psia (227.92°F)				P = 40 psia (267.22°F)			
Sat.	26.297	1077.7	1150.7	1.7549	20.093	1081.8	1156.2	1.7319	10.501	1092.1	1169.8	1.6766
240	27.429	1087.8	1163.9	1.7742	20.478	1086.5	1162.3	1.7406				
280	29.085	1102.4	1183.2	1.8010	21.739	1101.4	1181.9	1.7679	10.713	1097.3	1176.6	1.6858
320	30.722	1116.9	1202.2	1.8260	22.980	1116.1	1201.2	1.7933	11.363	1112.9	1197.1	1.7128
360	32.348	1131.3	1221.1	1.8496	24.209	1130.7	1220.2	1.8171	11.999	1128.1	1216.9	1.7376
400	33.965	1145.7	1239.9	1.8721	25.429	1145.1	1239.3	1.8398	12.625	1143.1	1236.5	1.7610
440	35.576	1160.1	1258.8	1.8936	26.644	1159.7	1258.3	1.8614	13.244	1157.9	1256.0	1.7831
500	37.986	1181.9	1287.3	1.9243	28.458	1181.6	1286.9	1.8922	14.165	1180.2	1285.0	1.8143
600	41.988	1218.7	1335.3	1.9718	31.467	1218.5	1334.9	1.9398	15.686	1217.5	1333.6	1.8625
700	45.981	1256.3	1383.9	2.0156	34.467	1256.1	1383.7	1.9837	17.197	1255.3	1382.6	1.9067
800	49.967	1294.6	1433.3	2.0565	37.461	1294.5	1433.1	2.0247	18.702	1293.9	1432.3	1.9478
1000	57.930	1374.0	1534.8	2.1312	43.438	1373.8	1534.6	2.0994	21.700	1373.4	1534.1	2.0227
1200	65.885	1456.9	1639.8	2.1986	49.407	1456.8	1639.7	2.1668	24.691	1456.5	1639.3	2.0902
1400	73.836	1543.6	1748.5	2.2604	55.373	1543.5	1748.4	2.2287	27.678	1543.3	1748.1	2.1522
1600	81.784	1634.0	1861.0	2.3178	61.335	1633.9	1860.9	2.2861	30.662	1633.7	1860.7	2.2096
	P = 60 psia (292.69°F)				P = 80 psia (312.02°F)				P = 100 psia (327.81°F)			
Sat.	7.1766	1098.1	1177.8	1.6442	5.4733	1102.3	1183.4	1.6212	4.4327	1105.5	1187.5	1.6032
320	7.4863	1109.6	1192.7	1.6636	5.5440	1105.9	1187.9	1.6271				
360	7.9259	1125.5	1213.5	1.6897	5.8876	1122.7	1209.9	1.6545	4.6628	1119.8	1206.1	1.6263
400	8.3548	1140.9	1233.7	1.7138	6.2187	1138.7	1230.8	1.6794	4.9359	1136.4	1227.8	1.6521
440	8.7766	1156.1	1253.6	1.7364	6.5420	1154.3	1251.2	1.7026	5.2006	1152.4	1248.7	1.6759
500	9.4005	1178.8	1283.1	1.7682	7.0177	1177.3	1281.2	1.7350	5.5876	1175.9	1279.3	1.7088
600	10.4256	1216.5	1332.2	1.8168	7.7951	1215.4	1330.8	1.7841	6.2167	1214.4	1329.4	1.7586
700	11.4401	1254.5	1381.6	1.8613	8.5616	1253.8	1380.5	1.8289	6.8344	1253.0	1379.5	1.8037
800	12.4484	1293.3	1431.5	1.9026	9.3218	1292.6	1430.6	1.8704	7.4457	1292.0	1429.8	1.8453
1000	14.4543	1373.0	1533.5	1.9777	10.8313	1372.6	1532.9	1.9457	8.6575	1372.2	1532.4	1.9208
1200	16.4525	1456.2	1638.9	2.0454	12.3331	1455.9	1638.5	2.0135	9.8615	1455.6	1638.1	1.9887
1400	18.4464	1543.0	1747.8	2.1073	13.8306	1542.8	1747.5	2.0755	11.0612	1542.6	1747.2	2.0508
1600	20.438	1633.5	1860.5	2.1648	15.3257	1633.3	1860.2	2.1330	12.2584	1633.2	1860.0	2.1083
1800	22.428	1727.6	1976.6	2.2187	16.8192	1727.5	1976.5	2.1869	13.4541	1727.3	1976.3	2.1622
2000	24.417	1825.2	2096.3	2.2694	18.3117	1825.0	2096.1	2.2376	14.6487	1824.9	2096.0	2.2130

*The temperature in parentheses is the saturation temperature at the specified pressure.

† Properties of saturated vapor at the specified pressure.

Superheated water (*Continued*)

H₂O

T °F	v ft³/lbm	u Btu/lbm	h Btu/lbm	s Btu/lbm · R	v ft³/lbm	u Btu/lbm	h Btu/lbm	s Btu/lbm · R	v ft³/lbm	u Btu/lbm	h Btu/lbm	s Btu/lbm · R
	P = 120 psia (341.25°F)				*P* = 140 psia (353.03°F)				*P* = 160 psia (363.54°F)			
Sat.	3.7289	1107.9	1190.8	1.5883	3.2202	1109.9	1193.4	1.5757	2.8347	1111.6	1195.5	1.5647
360	3.8446	1116.7	1202.1	1.6023	3.2584	1113.4	1197.8	1.5811				
400	4.0799	1134.0	1224.6	1.6292	3.4676	1131.5	1221.4	1.6092	3.0076	1129.0	1218.0	1.5914
450	4.3613	1154.5	1251.4	1.6594	3.7147	1152.6	1248.9	1.6403	3.2293	1150.7	1246.3	1.6234
500	4.6340	1174.4	1277.3	1.6872	3.9525	1172.9	1275.3	1.6686	3.4412	1171.4	1273.2	1.6522
550	4.9010	1193.9	1302.8	1.7131	4.1845	1192.7	1301.1	1.6948	3.6469	1191.4	1299.4	1.6788
600	5.1642	1213.4	1328.0	1.7375	4.4124	1212.3	1326.6	1.7195	3.8484	1211.3	1325.2	1.7037
700	5.6829	1252.2	1378.4	1.7829	4.8604	1251.4	1377.3	1.7652	4.2434	1250.6	1376.3	1.7498
800	6.1950	1291.4	1429.0	1.8247	5.3017	1290.8	1428.1	1.8072	4.6316	1290.2	1427.3	1.7920
1000	7.2083	1371.7	1531.8	1.9005	6.1732	1371.3	1531.3	1.8832	5.3968	1370.9	1530.7	1.8682
1200	8.2137	1455.3	1637.7	1.9684	7.0367	1455.0	1637.3	1.9512	6.1540	1454.7	1636.9	1.9363
1400	9.2149	1542.3	1746.9	2.0305	7.8961	1542.1	1746.6	2.0134	6.9070	1541.8	1746.3	1.9986
1600	10.2135	1633.0	1859.8	2.0881	8.7529	1632.8	1859.5	2.0711	7.6574	1632.6	1859.3	2.0563
1800	11.2106	1727.2	1976.1	2.1420	9.6082	1727.0	1975.9	2.1250	8.4063	1726.9	1975.7	2.1102
2000	12.2067	1824.8	2095.8	2.1928	10.4624	1824.6	2095.7	2.1758	9.1542	1824.5	2095.5	2.1610
	P = 180 psia (373.07°F)				*P* = 200 psia (381.80°F)				*P* = 225 psia (391.80°F)			
Sat.	2.5322	1113.0	1197.3	1.5548	2.2882	1114.1	1198.8	1.5460	2.0423	1115.3	1200.3	1.5360
400	2.6490	1126.3	1214.5	1.5752	2.3615	1123.5	1210.9	1.5602	2.0728	1119.7	1206.0	1.5427
450	2.8514	1148.7	1243.7	1.6082	2.5488	1146.7	1241.0	1.5943	2.2457	1144.1	1237.6	1.5783
500	3.0433	1169.8	1271.2	1.6376	2.7247	1168.2	1269.0	1.6243	2.4059	1166.2	1266.3	1.6091
550	3.2286	1190.2	1297.7	1.6646	2.8939	1188.9	1296.0	1.6516	2.5590	1187.2	1293.8	1.6370
600	3.4097	1210.2	1323.8	1.6897	3.0586	1209.1	1322.3	1.6771	2.7075	1207.7	1320.5	1.6628
700	3.7635	1249.8	1375.2	1.7361	3.3796	1249.0	1374.1	1.7238	2.9956	1248.0	1372.7	1.7099
800	4.1104	1289.5	1426.5	1.7785	3.6934	1288.9	1425.6	1.7664	3.2765	1288.1	1424.5	1.7528
900	4.4531	1329.7	1478.0	1.8179	4.0031	1329.2	1477.3	1.8059	3.5530	1328.5	1476.5	1.7925
1000	4.7929	1370.5	1530.1	1.8549	4.3099	1370.1	1529.6	1.8430	3.8268	1369.5	1528.9	1.8296
1200	5.4674	1454.3	1636.5	1.9231	4.9182	1454.0	1636.1	1.9113	4.3689	1453.6	1635.6	1.8981
1400	6.1377	1541.6	1746.0	1.9855	5.5222	1541.4	1745.7	1.9737	4.9068	1541.1	1745.4	1.9606
1600	6.8054	1632.4	1859.1	2.0432	6.1238	1632.2	1858.8	2.0315	5.4422	1632.0	1858.6	2.0184
1800	7.4716	1726.7	1975.6	2.0971	6.7238	1726.5	1975.4	2.0855	5.9760	1726.4	1975.2	2.0724
2000	8.1367	1824.4	2095.4	2.1479	7.3227	1824.3	2095.3	2.1363	6.5087	1824.1	2095.1	2.1232
	P = 250 psia (400.97°F)				*P* = 275 psia (409.45°F)				*P* = 300 psia (417.35°F)			
Sat.	1.8440	1116.3	1201.6	1.5270	1.6806	1117.0	1202.6	1.5187	1.5435	1117.7	1203.3	1.5111
450	2.0027	1141.3	1234.0	1.5636	1.8034	1138.5	1230.3	1.5499	1.6369	1135.6	1226.4	1.5369
500	2.1506	1164.1	1263.6	1.5953	1.9415	1162.0	1260.8	1.5825	1.7670	1159.8	1257.9	1.5706
550	2.2910	1185.6	1291.5	1.6237	2.0715	1183.9	1289.3	1.6115	1.8885	1182.1	1287.0	1.6001
600	2.4264	1206.3	1318.6	1.6499	2.1964	1204.9	1316.7	1.6380	2.0046	1203.5	1314.8	1.6270
650	2.5586	1226.8	1345.1	1.6743	2.3179	1225.6	1343.5	1.6627	2.1172	1224.4	1341.9	1.6520
700	2.6883	1247.0	1371.4	1.6974	2.4369	1246.0	1370.0	1.6860	2.2273	1244.9	1368.6	1.6755
800	2.9429	1287.3	1423.5	1.7406	2.6699	1286.5	1422.4	1.7294	2.4424	1285.7	1421.3	1.7192
900	3.1930	1327.9	1475.6	1.7804	2.8984	1327.3	1474.8	1.7694	2.6529	1326.6	1473.9	1.7593
1000	3.4403	1369.0	1528.2	1.8177	3.1241	1368.5	1527.4	1.8068	2.8605	1367.9	1526.7	1.7968
1200	3.9295	1453.3	1635.0	1.8863	3.5700	1452.9	1634.5	1.8755	3.2704	1452.5	1634.0	1.8657
1400	4.4144	1540.8	1745.0	1.9488	4.0116	1540.5	1744.6	1.9381	3.6759	1540.2	1744.2	1.9284
1600	4.8969	1631.7	1858.3	2.0066	4.4507	1631.5	1858.0	1.9960	4.0789	1631.3	1857.7	1.9863
1800	5.3777	1726.2	1974.9	2.0607	4.8882	1726.0	1974.7	2.0501	4.4803	1725.8	1974.5	2.0404
2000	5.8575	1823.9	2094.9	2.1116	5.3247	1823.8	2094.7	2.1010	4.8807	1823.6	2094.6	2.0913

Superheated water (*Continued*)

H₂O

T °F	v ft³/lbm	u Btu/lbm	h Btu/lbm	s Btu/ lbm · R	v ft³/lbm	u Btu/lbm	h Btu/lbm	s Btu/ lbm · R	v ft³/lbm	u Btu/lbm	h Btu/lbm	s Btu/ lbm · R
	P = 350 psia (431.74°F)				P = 400 psia (444.62°F)				P = 450 psia (456.31°F)			
Sat.	1.3263	1118.5	1204.4	1.4973	1.1617	1119.0	1205.0	1.4852	1.0324	1119.2	1205.2	1.4742
450	1.3739	1129.3	1218.3	1.5128	1.1747	1122.5	1209.4	1.4901				
500	1.4921	1155.2	1251.9	1.5487	1.2851	1150.4	1245.6	1.5288	1.1233	1145.4	1238.9	1.5103
550	1.6004	1178.6	1282.2	1.5795	1.3840	1174.9	1277.3	1.5610	1.2152	1171.1	1272.3	1.5441
600	1.7030	1200.6	1310.9	1.6073	1.4765	1197.6	1306.9	1.5897	1.3001	1194.6	1302.8	1.5737
650	1.8018	1221.9	1338.6	1.6328	1.5650	1219.4	1335.3	1.6158	1.3807	1216.9	1331.9	1.6005
700	1.8979	1242.8	1365.8	1.6567	1.6507	1240.7	1362.9	1.6401	1.4584	1238.5	1360.0	1.6253
800	2.0848	1284.1	1419.1	1.7009	1.8166	1282.5	1417.0	1.6849	1.6080	1280.8	1414.7	1.6706
900	2.2671	1325.3	1472.2	1.7414	1.9777	1324.0	1470.4	1.7257	1.7526	1322.7	1468.6	1.7117
1000	2.4464	1366.9	1525.3	1.7791	2.1358	1365.8	1523.9	1.7636	1.8942	1364.7	1522.4	1.7499
1200	2.7996	1451.7	1633.0	1.8483	2.4465	1450.9	1632.0	1.8331	2.1718	1450.1	1631.0	1.8196
1400	3.1484	1539.6	1743.5	1.9111	2.7527	1539.0	1742.7	1.8960	2.4450	1538.4	1742.0	1.8827
1600	3.4947	1630.8	1857.1	1.9691	3.0565	1630.3	1856.5	1.9541	2.7157	1629.8	1856.0	1.9409
1800	3.8394	1725.4	1974.0	2.0233	3.3586	1725.0	1973.6	2.0084	2.9847	1724.6	1973.2	1.9952
2000	4.1830	1823.3	2094.2	2.0742	3.6597	1823.0	2093.9	2.0594	3.2527	1822.6	2093.5	2.0462
	P = 500 psia (467.04°F)				P = 600 psia (486.24°F)				P = 700 psia (503.13°F)			
Sat.	0.92815	1119.1	1205.0	1.4642	0.77020	1118.3	1203.9	1.4463	0.65589	1116.9	1201.9	1.4305
500	0.99304	1140.1	1231.9	1.4928	0.79526	1128.2	1216.5	1.4596				
550	1.07974	1167.1	1267.0	1.5284	0.87542	1158.7	1255.9	1.4996	0.72799	1149.5	1243.8	1.4730
600	1.15876	1191.4	1298.6	1.5590	0.94605	1184.9	1289.9	1.5325	0.79332	1177.9	1280.7	1.5087
650	1.23312	1214.3	1328.4	1.5865	1.01133	1209.0	1321.3	1.5614	0.85242	1203.4	1313.8	1.5393
700	1.30440	1236.4	1357.0	1.6117	1.07316	1231.9	1351.0	1.5877	0.90769	1227.2	1344.8	1.5666
800	1.44097	1279.2	1412.5	1.6576	1.19038	1275.8	1408.0	1.6348	1.01125	1272.4	1403.4	1.6150
900	1.57252	1321.4	1466.9	1.6992	1.30230	1318.7	1463.3	1.6771	1.10921	1316.0	1459.7	1.6581
1000	1.70094	1363.6	1521.0	1.7376	1.41097	1361.4	1518.1	1.7160	1.20381	1359.2	1515.2	1.6974
1100	1.82726	1406.2	1575.3	1.7735	1.51749	1404.4	1572.9	1.7522	1.29621	1402.5	1570.4	1.7341
1200	1.95211	1449.4	1630.0	1.8075	1.62252	1447.8	1627.9	1.7865	1.38709	1446.2	1625.9	1.7685
1400	2.1988	1537.8	1741.2	1.8708	1.82957	1536.6	1739.7	1.8501	1.56580	1535.4	1738.2	1.8324
1600	2.4430	1629.4	1855.4	1.9291	2.0340	1628.4	1854.2	1.9085	1.74192	1627.5	1853.1	1.8911
1800	2.6856	1724.2	1972.7	1.9834	2.2369	1723.4	1971.8	1.9630	1.91643	1722.7	1970.9	1.9457
2000	2.9271	1822.3	2093.1	2.0345	2.4387	1821.7	2092.4	2.0141	2.08987	1821.0	2091.7	1.9969
	P = 800 psia (518.27°F)				P = 1000 psia (544.65°F)				P = 1250 psia (572.45°F)			
Sat.	0.56920	1115.0	1199.3	1.4162	0.44604	1110.1	1192.6	1.3906	0.34549	1102.0	1181.9	1.3623
550	0.61586	1139.4	1230.5	1.4476	0.45375	1115.2	1199.2	1.3972				
600	0.67799	1170.5	1270.9	1.4866	0.51431	1154.1	1249.3	1.4457	0.37894	1129.5	1217.2	1.3961
650	0.73279	1197.6	1306.0	1.5191	0.56411	1185.1	1289.5	1.4827	0.42703	1167.5	1266.3	1.4414
700	0.78330	1222.4	1338.4	1.5476	0.60844	1212.4	1325.0	1.5140	0.46735	1198.7	1306.8	1.4771
750	0.83102	1246.0	1369.1	1.5735	0.64944	1237.6	1357.8	1.5418	0.50344	1226.4	1342.9	1.5076
800	0.87678	1268.9	1398.7	1.5975	0.68821	1261.7	1389.0	1.5670	0.53687	1252.2	1376.4	1.5347
900	0.96434	1313.3	1456.0	1.6413	0.76136	1307.7	1448.6	1.6126	0.59876	1300.5	1439.0	1.5826
1000	1.04841	1357.0	1512.2	1.6812	0.83078	1352.5	1506.2	1.6535	0.65656	1346.7	1498.6	1.6249
1100	1.13024	1400.7	1568.0	1.7181	0.89783	1396.9	1563.1	1.6911	0.71184	1392.2	1556.8	1.6635
1200	1.21051	1444.6	1623.8	1.7528	0.96327	1441.4	1619.7	1.7263	0.76545	1437.4	1614.5	1.6993
1400	1.36797	1534.2	1736.7	1.8170	1.09101	1531.8	1733.7	1.7911	0.86944	1528.7	1729.8	1.7649
1600	1.52283	1626.5	1851.9	1.8759	1.21610	1624.6	1849.6	1.8504	0.97072	1622.2	1846.7	1.8246
1800	1.67606	1721.9	1970.0	1.9306	1.33956	1720.3	1968.2	1.9053	1.07036	1718.4	1966.0	1.8799
2000	1.82823	1820.4	2091.0	1.9819	1.46194	1819.1	2089.6	1.9568	1.16892	1817.5	2087.9	1.9315

Superheated water (*Concluded*)

H$_2$O

T	v	u	h	s	v	u	h	s	v	u	h	s
°F	ft³/lbm	Btu/lbm	Btu/lbm	Btu/ lbm·R	ft³/lbm	Btu/lbm	Btu/lbm	Btu/ lbm·R	ft³/lbm	Btu/lbm	Btu/lbm	Btu/ lbm·R
	P = 1500 psia (596.26°F)				*P* = 1750 psia (617.17°F)				*P* = 2000 psia (635.85°F)			
Sat.	0.27695	1092.1	1169.0	1.3362	0.22681	1080.5	1153.9	1.3112	0.18815	1066.8	1136.4	1.2863
600	0.28189	1097.2	1175.4	1.3423								
650	0.33310	1147.2	1239.7	1.4016	0.26292	1122.8	1207.9	1.3607	0.20586	1091.4	1167.6	1.3146
700	0.37198	1183.6	1286.9	1.4433	0.30252	1166.8	1264.7	1.4108	0.24894	1147.6	1239.8	1.3783
750	0.40535	1214.4	1326.9	1.4771	0.33455	1201.5	1309.8	1.4489	0.28074	1187.4	1291.3	1.4218
800	0.43550	1242.2	1363.1	1.5064	0.36266	1231.7	1349.1	1.4807	0.30763	1220.5	1334.3	1.4567
850	0.46356	1268.2	1396.9	1.5328	0.38835	1259.3	1385.1	1.5088	0.33169	1250.0	1372.8	1.4867
900	0.49015	1293.1	1429.2	1.5569	0.41238	1285.4	1419.0	1.5341	0.35390	1277.5	1408.5	1.5134
1000	0.54031	1340.9	1490.8	1.6007	0.45719	1334.9	1482.9	1.5796	0.39479	1328.7	1474.9	1.5606
1100	0.58781	1387.3	1550.5	1.6402	0.49917	1382.4	1544.1	1.6201	0.43266	1377.5	1537.6	1.6021
1200	0.63355	1433.3	1609.2	1.6767	0.53932	1429.2	1603.9	1.6572	0.46864	1425.1	1598.5	1.6400
1400	0.72172	1525.7	1726.0	1.7432	0.61621	1522.6	1722.1	1.7245	0.53708	1519.5	1718.3	1.7081
1600	0.80714	1619.8	1843.8	1.8033	0.69031	1617.4	1840.9	1.7852	0.60269	1615.0	1838.0	1.7693
1800	0.89090	1716.4	1963.7	1.8589	0.76273	1714.5	1961.5	1.8410	0.66660	1712.5	1959.2	1.8255
2000	0.97358	1815.9	2086.1	1.9108	0.83406	1814.2	2084.3	1.8931	0.72942	1812.6	2082.6	1.8778
	P = 2500 psia (668.17°F)				*P* = 3000 psia (695.41°F)				*P* = 3500 psia			
Sat.	0.13076	1031.2	1091.7	1.2330	0.08460	969.8	1016.8	1.1587				
650									0.02492	663.7	679.9	0.8632
700	0.16849	1098.4	1176.3	1.3072	0.09838	1005.3	1059.9	1.1960	0.03065	760.0	779.9	0.9511
750	0.20327	1154.9	1249.0	1.3686	0.14840	1114.1	1196.5	1.3118	0.10460	1057.6	1125.4	1.2434
800	0.22949	1195.9	1302.0	1.4116	0.17601	1167.5	1265.3	1.3676	0.13639	1134.3	1222.6	1.3224
850	0.25174	1230.1	1346.6	1.4463	0.19771	1208.2	1317.9	1.4086	0.15847	1183.8	1286.5	1.3721
900	0.27165	1260.7	1386.4	1.4761	0.21640	1242.8	1362.9	1.4423	0.17659	1223.4	1337.8	1.4106
950	0.29001	1289.1	1423.3	1.5028	0.23321	1273.9	1403.3	1.4716	0.19245	1257.8	1382.4	1.4428
1000	0.30726	1316.1	1458.2	1.5271	0.24876	1302.8	1440.9	1.4978	0.20687	1289.0	1423.0	1.4711
1100	0.33949	1367.3	1524.4	1.5710	0.27732	1356.8	1510.8	1.5441	0.23289	1346.1	1496.9	1.5201
1200	0.36966	1416.6	1587.6	1.6103	0.30367	1408.0	1576.6	1.5850	0.25654	1399.3	1565.4	1.5627
1400	0.42631	1513.3	1710.5	1.6802	0.35249	1507.0	1702.7	1.6567	0.29978	1500.7	1694.8	1.6364
1600	0.48004	1610.1	1832.2	1.7424	0.39830	1605.3	1826.4	1.7199	0.33994	1600.4	1820.5	1.7006
1800	0.53205	1708.6	1954.8	1.7991	0.44237	1704.7	1950.3	1.7773	0.37833	1700.8	1945.8	1.7586
2000	0.58295	1809.4	2079.1	1.8518	0.48532	1806.1	2075.6	1.8304	0.41561	1802.9	2072.1	1.8121
	P = 4000 psia				*P* = 5000 psia				*P* = 6000 psia			
650	0.02448	657.9	676.1	0.8577	0.02379	648.3	670.3	0.8485	0.02325	640.3	666.1	0.8408
700	0.02871	742.3	763.6	0.9347	0.02678	721.8	746.6	0.9156	0.02564	708.1	736.5	0.9028
750	0.06370	962.1	1009.2	1.1410	0.03373	821.8	853.0	1.0054	0.02981	788.7	821.8	0.9747
800	0.10520	1094.2	1172.1	1.2734	0.05937	986.9	1041.8	1.1581	0.03949	897.1	941.0	1.0711
850	0.12848	1156.7	1251.8	1.3355	0.08551	1092.4	1171.5	1.2593	0.05815	1018.6	1083.1	1.1819
900	0.14647	1202.5	1310.9	1.3799	0.10390	1155.9	1252.1	1.3198	0.07584	1103.5	1187.7	1.2603
950	0.16176	1240.7	1360.5	1.4157	0.11863	1203.9	1313.6	1.3643	0.09010	1163.7	1263.7	1.3153
1000	0.17538	1274.6	1404.4	1.4463	0.13128	1244.0	1365.5	1.4004	0.10208	1211.4	1324.7	1.3578
1100	0.19957	1335.1	1482.8	1.4983	0.15298	1312.2	1453.8	1.4590	0.12211	1288.4	1424.0	1.4237
1200	0.22121	1390.3	1554.1	1.5426	0.17185	1372.1	1531.1	1.5070	0.13911	1353.4	1507.8	1.4758
1300	0.24128	1443.0	1621.6	1.5821	0.18902	1427.8	1602.7	1.5490	0.15434	1412.5	1583.8	1.5203
1400	0.26028	1494.3	1687.0	1.6182	0.20508	1481.4	1671.1	1.5868	0.16841	1468.4	1655.4	1.5598
1600	0.29620	1595.5	1814.7	1.6835	0.23505	1585.6	1803.1	1.6542	0.19438	1575.7	1791.5	1.6294
1800	0.33033	1696.8	1941.4	1.7422	0.26320	1689.0	1932.5	1.7142	0.21853	1681.1	1923.7	1.6907
2000	0.36335	1799.7	2068.6	1.7961	0.29023	1793.2	2061.7	1.7689	0.24155	1786.7	2054.9	1.7463

TABLE A–7E

Compressed liquid water

T °F	v ft³/lbm	u Btu/lbm	h Btu/lbm	s Btu/lbm·R	v ft³/lbm	u Btu/lbm	h Btu/lbm	s Btu/lbm·R	v ft³/lbm	u Btu/lbm	h Btu/lbm	s Btu/lbm·R
	P = 500 psia (467.04°F)				P = 1000 psia (544.65°F)				P = 1500 psia (596.26°F)			
Sat.	0.019750	447.68	449.51	0.64900	0.021595	538.58	542.57	0.74341	0.023456	605.07	611.58	0.80836
32	0.015994	0.01	1.49	0.00001	0.015966	0.03	2.99	0.00005	0.015939	0.05	4.48	0.00008
50	0.015998	18.03	19.51	0.03601	0.015972	17.99	20.95	0.03593	0.015946	17.95	22.38	0.03584
100	0.016107	67.86	69.35	0.12930	0.016083	67.69	70.67	0.12899	0.016059	67.53	71.98	0.12869
150	0.016317	117.70	119.21	0.21462	0.016292	117.42	120.43	0.21416	0.016267	117.14	121.66	0.21369
200	0.016607	167.70	169.24	0.29349	0.016580	167.31	170.38	0.29289	0.016553	166.92	171.52	0.29229
250	0.016972	218.04	219.61	0.36708	0.016941	217.51	220.65	0.36634	0.016911	217.00	221.69	0.36560
300	0.017417	268.92	270.53	0.43641	0.017380	268.24	271.46	0.43551	0.017345	267.57	272.39	0.43463
350	0.017954	320.64	322.30	0.50240	0.017910	319.77	323.08	0.50132	0.017866	318.91	323.87	0.50025
400	0.018609	373.61	375.33	0.56595	0.018552	372.48	375.91	0.56463	0.018496	371.37	376.51	0.56333
450	0.019425	428.44	430.24	0.62802	0.019347	426.93	430.51	0.62635	0.019271	425.47	430.82	0.62472
500					0.020368	484.03	487.80	0.68764	0.020258	482.01	487.63	0.68550
550									0.021595	542.50	548.50	0.74731
	P = 2000 psia (635.85°F)				P = 3000 psia (695.41°F)				P = 5000 psia			
Sat.	0.025634	662.33	671.82	0.86224	0.034335	783.39	802.45	0.97321				
32	0.015912	0.07	5.96	0.00010	0.015859	0.10	8.90	0.00011	0.015756	0.13	14.71	0.00002
50	0.015921	17.91	23.80	0.03574	0.015870	17.83	26.64	0.03554	0.015773	17.65	32.25	0.03505
100	0.016035	67.36	73.30	0.12838	0.015988	67.04	75.91	0.12776	0.015897	66.41	81.12	0.12652
200	0.016527	166.54	172.66	0.29170	0.016475	165.79	174.94	0.29053	0.016375	164.36	179.51	0.28824
300	0.017310	266.92	273.33	0.43376	0.017242	265.65	275.22	0.43204	0.017112	263.24	279.07	0.42874
400	0.018442	370.30	377.12	0.56205	0.018338	368.22	378.41	0.55959	0.018145	364.35	381.14	0.55492
450	0.019199	424.06	431.16	0.62314	0.019062	421.36	431.94	0.62010	0.018812	416.40	433.80	0.61445
500	0.020154	480.08	487.54	0.68346	0.019960	476.45	487.53	0.67958	0.019620	469.94	488.10	0.67254
560	0.021739	552.21	560.26	0.75692	0.021405	546.59	558.47	0.75126	0.020862	537.08	556.38	0.74154
600	0.023317	605.77	614.40	0.80898	0.022759	597.42	610.06	0.80086	0.021943	584.42	604.72	0.78803
640					0.024765	654.52	668.27	0.85476	0.023358	634.95	656.56	0.83603
680					0.028821	728.63	744.64	0.92288	0.025366	690.67	714.14	0.88745
700									0.026777	721.78	746.56	0.91564

TABLE A–8E

Saturated ice—water vapor

Temp., T °F	Sat. press., P_{sat} psia	Specific volume, ft³/lbm		Internal energy, Btu/lbm			Enthalpy, Btu/lbm			Entropy, Btu/lbm · R		
		Sat. ice, v_i	Sat. vapor, v_g	Sat. ice, u_i	Subl., u_{ig}	Sat. vapor, u_g	Sat. ice, h_i	Subl., h_{ig}	Sat. vapor, h_g	Sat. ice, s_i	Subl., s_{ig}	Sat. vapor, s_g
32.018	0.08871	0.01747	3299.6	−143.34	1164.2	1020.9	−143.34	1218.3	1075.0	−0.29146	2.4779	2.1864
32	0.08864	0.01747	3302.6	−143.35	1164.2	1020.9	−143.35	1218.4	1075.0	−0.29148	2.4779	2.1865
30	0.08086	0.01747	3605.8	−144.35	1164.6	1020.2	−144.35	1218.5	1074.2	−0.29353	2.4883	2.1948
25	0.06405	0.01746	4505.8	−146.85	1165.4	1018.6	−146.85	1218.8	1072.0	−0.29865	2.5146	2.2160
20	0.05049	0.01746	5657.6	−149.32	1166.2	1016.9	−149.32	1219.1	1069.8	−0.30377	2.5414	2.2376
15	0.03960	0.01745	7138.9	−151.76	1167.0	1015.2	−151.76	1219.3	1067.6	−0.30889	2.5687	2.2598
10	0.03089	0.01744	9054.0	−154.18	1167.8	1013.6	−154.18	1219.5	1065.4	−0.31401	2.5965	2.2825
5	0.02397	0.01743	11,543	−156.57	1168.5	1011.9	−156.57	1219.7	1063.1	−0.31913	2.6248	2.3057
0	0.01850	0.01743	14,797	−158.94	1169.2	1010.3	−158.94	1219.9	1060.9	−0.32426	2.6537	2.3295
−5	0.01420	0.01742	19,075	−161.28	1169.9	1008.6	−161.28	1220.0	1058.7	−0.32938	2.6832	2.3538
−10	0.01083	0.01741	24,731	−163.60	1170.6	1007.0	−163.60	1220.1	1056.5	−0.33451	2.7133	2.3788
−15	0.00821	0.01740	32,257	−165.90	1171.2	1005.3	−165.90	1220.2	1054.3	−0.33964	2.7440	2.4044
−20	0.00619	0.01740	42,335	−168.16	1171.8	1003.6	−168.16	1220.3	1052.1	−0.34478	2.7754	2.4306
−25	0.00463	0.01739	55,917	−170.41	1172.4	1002.0	−170.41	1220.3	1049.9	−0.34991	2.8074	2.4575
−30	0.00344	0.01738	74,345	−172.63	1173.0	1000.3	−172.63	1220.3	1047.7	−0.35505	2.8401	2.4850
−35	0.00254	0.01738	99,526	−174.83	1173.5	998.7	−174.83	1220.3	1045.5	−0.36019	2.8735	2.5133
−40	0.00186	0.01737	134,182	−177.00	1174.0	997.0	−177.00	1220.3	1043.3	−0.36534	2.9076	2.5423

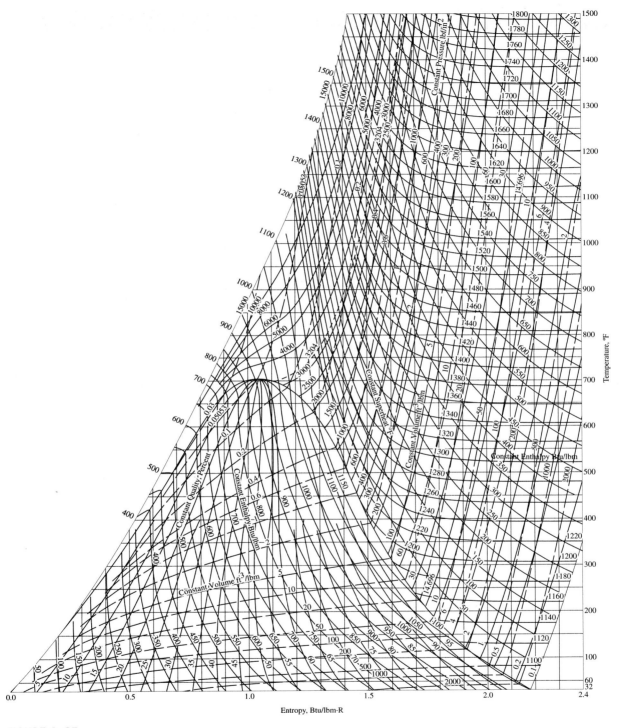

FIGURE A–9E

T-s diagram for water.

Source: Joseph H. Keenan, Frederick G. Keyes, Philip G. Hill, and Joan G. Moore, Steam Tables *(New York: John Wiley & Sons, 1969).*

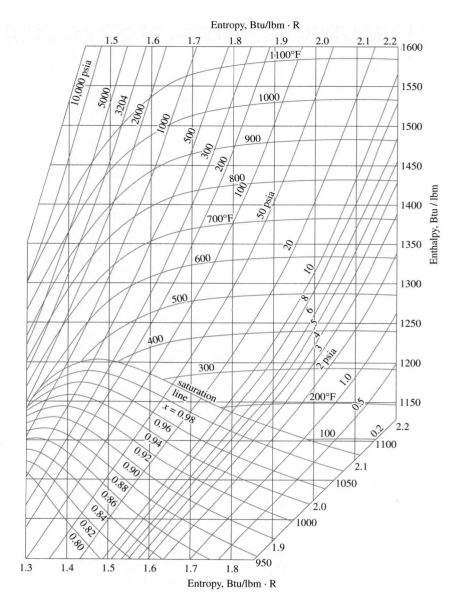

FIGURE A–10E

Mollier diagram for water.

Source: Joseph H. Keenan, Frederick G. Keyes, Philip G. Hill, and Joan G. Moore, Steam Tables *(New York: John Wiley & Sons, 1969).*

TABLE A–11E

Saturated refrigerant-134a—Temperature table

Temp., T °F	Sat. press., P_{sat} psia	Specific volume, ft³/lbm		Internal energy, Btu/lbm			Enthalpy, Btu/lbm				Entropy, Btu/lbm·R		
		Sat. liquid, v_f	Sat. vapor, v_g	Sat. liquid, u_f	Evap., u_{fg}	Sat. vapor, u_g	Sat. liquid, h_f	Evap., h_{fg}	Sat. vapor, h_g	Sat. liquid, s_f	Evap., s_{fg}	Sat. vapor, s_g
−40	7.432	0.01130	5.7796	−0.016	89.167	89.15	0.000	97.100	97.10	0.00000	0.23135	0.23135
−35	8.581	0.01136	5.0509	1.484	88.352	89.84	1.502	96.354	97.86	0.00355	0.22687	0.23043
−30	9.869	0.01143	4.4300	2.990	87.532	90.52	3.011	95.601	98.61	0.00708	0.22248	0.22956
−25	11.306	0.01150	3.8988	4.502	86.706	91.21	4.526	94.839	99.36	0.01058	0.21817	0.22875
−20	12.906	0.01156	3.4426	6.019	85.874	91.89	6.047	94.068	100.12	0.01405	0.21394	0.22798
−15	14.680	0.01163	3.0494	7.543	85.036	92.58	7.574	93.288	100.86	0.01749	0.20978	0.22727
−10	16.642	0.01171	2.7091	9.073	84.191	93.26	9.109	92.498	101.61	0.02092	0.20569	0.22660
−5	18.806	0.01178	2.4137	10.609	83.339	93.95	10.650	91.698	102.35	0.02431	0.20166	0.22598
0	21.185	0.01185	2.1564	12.152	82.479	94.63	12.199	90.886	103.08	0.02769	0.19770	0.22539
5	23.793	0.01193	1.9316	13.702	81.610	95.31	13.755	90.062	103.82	0.03104	0.19380	0.22485
10	26.646	0.01201	1.7345	15.259	80.733	95.99	15.318	89.226	104.54	0.03438	0.18996	0.22434
15	29.759	0.01209	1.5612	16.823	79.846	96.67	16.889	88.377	105.27	0.03769	0.18617	0.22386
20	33.147	0.01217	1.4084	18.394	78.950	97.34	18.469	87.514	105.98	0.04098	0.18243	0.22341
25	36.826	0.01225	1.2732	19.973	78.043	98.02	20.056	86.636	106.69	0.04426	0.17874	0.22300
30	40.813	0.01234	1.1534	21.560	77.124	98.68	21.653	85.742	107.40	0.04752	0.17509	0.22260
35	45.124	0.01242	1.0470	23.154	76.195	99.35	23.258	84.833	108.09	0.05076	0.17148	0.22224
40	49.776	0.01251	0.95205	24.757	75.253	100.01	24.873	83.907	108.78	0.05398	0.16791	0.22189
45	54.787	0.01261	0.86727	26.369	74.298	100.67	26.497	82.963	109.46	0.05720	0.16437	0.22157
50	60.175	0.01270	0.79136	27.990	73.329	101.32	28.131	82.000	110.13	0.06039	0.16087	0.22127
55	65.957	0.01280	0.72323	29.619	72.346	101.97	29.775	81.017	110.79	0.06358	0.15740	0.22098
60	72.152	0.01290	0.66195	31.258	71.347	102.61	31.431	80.013	111.44	0.06675	0.15396	0.22070
65	78.780	0.01301	0.60671	32.908	70.333	103.24	33.097	78.988	112.09	0.06991	0.15053	0.22044
70	85.858	0.01312	0.55681	34.567	69.301	103.87	34.776	77.939	112.71	0.07306	0.14713	0.22019
75	93.408	0.01323	0.51165	36.237	68.251	104.49	36.466	76.866	113.33	0.07620	0.14375	0.21995
80	101.45	0.01334	0.47069	37.919	67.181	105.10	38.169	75.767	113.94	0.07934	0.14038	0.21972
85	110.00	0.01347	0.43348	39.612	66.091	105.70	39.886	74.641	114.53	0.08246	0.13703	0.21949
90	119.08	0.01359	0.39959	41.317	64.979	106.30	41.617	73.485	115.10	0.08559	0.13368	0.21926
95	128.72	0.01372	0.36869	43.036	63.844	106.88	43.363	72.299	115.66	0.08870	0.13033	0.21904
100	138.93	0.01386	0.34045	44.768	62.683	107.45	45.124	71.080	116.20	0.09182	0.12699	0.21881
105	149.73	0.01400	0.31460	46.514	61.496	108.01	46.902	69.825	116.73	0.09493	0.12365	0.21858
110	161.16	0.01415	0.29090	48.276	60.279	108.56	48.698	68.533	117.23	0.09804	0.12029	0.21834
115	173.23	0.01430	0.26913	50.054	59.031	109.08	50.512	67.200	117.71	0.10116	0.11693	0.21809
120	185.96	0.01446	0.24909	51.849	57.749	109.60	52.346	65.823	118.17	0.10428	0.11354	0.21782
130	213.53	0.01482	0.21356	55.495	55.071	110.57	56.080	62.924	119.00	0.11054	0.10670	0.21724
140	244.06	0.01521	0.18315	59.226	52.216	111.44	59.913	59.801	119.71	0.11684	0.09971	0.21655
150	277.79	0.01567	0.15692	63.059	49.144	112.20	63.864	56.405	120.27	0.12321	0.09251	0.21572
160	314.94	0.01619	0.13410	67.014	45.799	112.81	67.958	52.671	120.63	0.12970	0.08499	0.21469
170	355.80	0.01681	0.11405	71.126	42.097	113.22	72.233	48.499	120.73	0.13634	0.07701	0.21335
180	400.66	0.01759	0.09618	75.448	37.899	113.35	76.752	43.726	120.48	0.14323	0.06835	0.21158
190	449.90	0.01860	0.07990	80.082	32.950	113.03	81.631	38.053	119.68	0.15055	0.05857	0.20911
200	504.00	0.02009	0.06441	85.267	26.651	111.92	87.140	30.785	117.93	0.15867	0.04666	0.20533
210	563.76	0.02309	0.04722	91.986	16.498	108.48	94.395	19.015	113.41	0.16922	0.02839	0.19761

Source: Tables A–11E through A–13E are generated using the Engineering Equation Solver (EES) software developed by S. A. Klein and F. L. Alvarado. The routine used in calculations is the R134a, which is based on the fundamental equation of state developed by R. Tillner-Roth and H.D. Baehr, "An International Standard Formulation for the Thermodynamic Properties of 1,1,1,2-Tetrafluoroethane (HFC-134a) for Temperatures from 170 K to 455 K and Pressures up to 70 MPa," *J. Phys. Chem, Ref. Data*, Vol. 23, No. 5, 1994. The enthalpy and entropy values of saturated liquid are set to zero at −40°C (and −40°F).

TABLE A–12E

Saturated refrigerant-134a—Pressure table

Press., P psia	Sat. temp., T °F	Specific volume, ft³/lbm Sat. liquid, v_f	Sat. vapor, v_g	Internal energy, Btu/lbm Sat. liquid, u_f	Evap., u_{fg}	Sat. vapor, u_g	Enthalpy, Btu/lbm Sat. liquid, h_f	Evap., h_{fg}	Sat. vapor, h_g	Entropy, Btu/lbm · R Sat. liquid, s_f	Evap., s_{fg}	Sat. vapor, s_g
5	−53.09	0.01113	8.3785	−3.918	91.280	87.36	−3.907	99.022	95.11	−0.00945	0.24353	0.23408
10	−29.52	0.01144	4.3753	3.135	87.453	90.59	3.156	95.528	98.68	0.00742	0.22206	0.22948
15	−14.15	0.01165	2.9880	7.803	84.893	92.70	7.835	93.155	100.99	0.01808	0.20908	0.22715
20	−2.43	0.01182	2.2772	11.401	82.898	94.30	11.445	91.282	102.73	0.02605	0.19962	0.22567
25	7.17	0.01196	1.8429	14.377	81.231	95.61	14.432	89.701	104.13	0.03249	0.19213	0.22462
30	15.37	0.01209	1.5492	16.939	79.780	96.72	17.006	88.313	105.32	0.03793	0.18589	0.22383
35	22.57	0.01221	1.3369	19.205	78.485	97.69	19.284	87.064	106.35	0.04267	0.18053	0.22319
40	29.01	0.01232	1.1760	21.246	77.307	98.55	21.337	85.920	107.26	0.04688	0.17580	0.22268
45	34.86	0.01242	1.0497	23.110	76.221	99.33	23.214	84.858	108.07	0.05067	0.17158	0.22225
50	40.23	0.01252	0.94791	24.832	75.209	100.04	24.948	83.863	108.81	0.05413	0.16774	0.22188
55	45.20	0.01261	0.86400	26.435	74.258	100.69	26.564	82.924	109.49	0.05733	0.16423	0.22156
60	49.84	0.01270	0.79361	27.939	73.360	101.30	28.080	82.030	110.11	0.06029	0.16098	0.22127
65	54.20	0.01279	0.73370	29.357	72.505	101.86	29.510	81.176	110.69	0.06307	0.15796	0.22102
70	58.30	0.01287	0.68205	30.700	71.688	102.39	30.867	80.357	111.22	0.06567	0.15512	0.22080
75	62.19	0.01295	0.63706	31.979	70.905	102.88	32.159	79.567	111.73	0.06813	0.15245	0.22059
80	65.89	0.01303	0.59750	33.201	70.151	103.35	33.394	78.804	112.20	0.07047	0.14993	0.22040
85	69.41	0.01310	0.56244	34.371	69.424	103.79	34.577	78.064	112.64	0.07269	0.14753	0.22022
90	72.78	0.01318	0.53113	35.495	68.719	104.21	35.715	77.345	113.06	0.07481	0.14525	0.22006
95	76.02	0.01325	0.50301	36.578	68.035	104.61	36.811	76.645	113.46	0.07684	0.14307	0.21991
100	79.12	0.01332	0.47760	37.623	67.371	104.99	37.869	75.962	113.83	0.07879	0.14097	0.21976
110	85.00	0.01347	0.43347	39.612	66.091	105.70	39.886	74.641	114.53	0.08246	0.13703	0.21949
120	90.49	0.01360	0.39644	41.485	64.869	106.35	41.787	73.371	115.16	0.08589	0.13335	0.21924
130	95.64	0.01374	0.36491	43.258	63.696	106.95	43.589	72.144	115.73	0.08911	0.12990	0.21901
140	100.51	0.01387	0.33771	44.945	62.564	107.51	45.304	70.954	116.26	0.09214	0.12665	0.21879
150	105.12	0.01400	0.31401	46.556	61.467	108.02	46.945	69.795	116.74	0.09501	0.12357	0.21857
160	109.50	0.01413	0.29316	48.101	60.401	108.50	48.519	68.662	117.18	0.09774	0.12062	0.21836
170	113.69	0.01426	0.27466	49.586	59.362	108.95	50.035	67.553	117.59	0.10034	0.11781	0.21815
180	117.69	0.01439	0.25813	51.018	58.345	109.36	51.497	66.464	117.96	0.10284	0.11511	0.21795
190	121.53	0.01452	0.24327	52.402	57.349	109.75	52.912	65.392	118.30	0.10524	0.11250	0.21774
200	125.22	0.01464	0.22983	53.743	56.371	110.11	54.285	64.335	118.62	0.10754	0.10998	0.21753
220	132.21	0.01490	0.20645	56.310	54.458	110.77	56.917	62.256	119.17	0.11192	0.10517	0.21710
240	138.73	0.01516	0.18677	58.746	52.591	111.34	59.419	60.213	119.63	0.11603	0.10061	0.21665
260	144.85	0.01543	0.16996	61.071	50.757	111.83	61.813	58.192	120.00	0.11992	0.09625	0.21617
280	150.62	0.01570	0.15541	63.301	48.945	112.25	64.115	56.184	120.30	0.12362	0.09205	0.21567
300	156.09	0.01598	0.14266	65.452	47.143	112.60	66.339	54.176	120.52	0.12715	0.08797	0.21512
350	168.64	0.01672	0.11664	70.554	42.627	113.18	71.638	49.099	120.74	0.13542	0.07814	0.21356
400	179.86	0.01757	0.09642	75.385	37.963	113.35	76.686	43.798	120.48	0.14314	0.06848	0.21161
450	190.02	0.01860	0.07987	80.092	32.939	113.03	81.641	38.041	119.68	0.15056	0.05854	0.20911
500	199.29	0.01995	0.06551	84.871	27.168	112.04	86.718	31.382	118.10	0.15805	0.04762	0.20566

R-134a

TABLE A–13E

Superheated refrigerant-134a

T °F	v ft³/lbm	u Btu/lbm	h Btu/lbm	s Btu/ lbm · R	v ft³/lbm	u Btu/lbm	h Btu/lbm	s Btu/ lbm · R	v ft³/lbm	u Btu/lbm	h Btu/lbm	s Btu/ lbm · R
	$P = 10$ psia ($T_{sat} = -29.52°F$)				$P = 15$ psia ($T_{sat} = -14.15°F$)				$P = 20$ psia ($T_{sat} = -2.43°F$)			
Sat.	4.3753	90.59	98.68	0.22948	2.9880	92.70	100.99	0.22715	2.2772	94.30	102.73	0.22567
−20	4.4856	92.13	100.43	0.23350								
0	4.7135	95.41	104.14	0.24174	3.1001	95.08	103.68	0.23310	2.2922	94.72	103.20	0.22671
20	4.9380	98.77	107.91	0.24976	3.2551	98.48	107.52	0.24127	2.4130	98.19	107.12	0.23504
40	5.1600	102.20	111.75	0.25761	3.4074	101.95	111.41	0.24922	2.5306	101.70	111.07	0.24311
60	5.3802	105.72	115.67	0.26531	3.5577	105.50	115.38	0.25700	2.6461	105.28	115.07	0.25097
80	5.5989	109.32	119.68	0.27288	3.7064	109.13	119.42	0.26463	2.7600	108.93	119.15	0.25866
100	5.8165	113.01	123.78	0.28033	3.8540	112.84	123.54	0.27212	2.8726	112.66	123.29	0.26621
120	6.0331	116.79	127.96	0.28767	4.0006	116.63	127.74	0.27950	2.9842	116.47	127.52	0.27363
140	6.2490	120.66	132.22	0.29490	4.1464	120.51	132.02	0.28677	3.0950	120.37	131.82	0.28093
160	6.4642	124.61	136.57	0.30203	4.2915	124.48	136.39	0.29393	3.2051	124.35	136.21	0.28812
180	6.6789	128.65	141.01	0.30908	4.4361	128.53	140.84	0.30100	3.3146	128.41	140.67	0.29521
200	6.8930	132.77	145.53	0.31604	4.5802	132.66	145.37	0.30798	3.4237	132.55	145.22	0.30221
220	7.1068	136.98	150.13	0.32292	4.7239	136.88	149.99	0.31487	3.5324	136.78	149.85	0.30912
	$P = 30$ psia ($T_{sat} = 15.37°F$)				$P = 40$ psia ($T_{sat} = 29.01°F$)				$P = 50$ psia ($T_{sat} = 40.23°F$)			
Sat.	1.5492	96.72	105.32	0.22383	1.1760	98.55	107.26	0.22268	0.9479	100.04	108.81	0.22188
20	1.5691	97.56	106.27	0.22581								
40	1.6528	101.17	110.35	0.23414	1.2126	100.61	109.58	0.22738				
60	1.7338	104.82	114.45	0.24219	1.2768	104.34	113.79	0.23565	1.0019	103.84	113.11	0.23031
80	1.8130	108.53	118.59	0.25002	1.3389	108.11	118.02	0.24363	1.0540	107.68	117.43	0.23847
100	1.8908	112.30	122.80	0.25767	1.3995	111.93	122.29	0.25140	1.1043	111.55	121.77	0.24637
120	1.9675	116.15	127.07	0.26517	1.4588	115.82	126.62	0.25900	1.1534	115.48	126.16	0.25406
140	2.0434	120.08	131.42	0.27254	1.5173	119.78	131.01	0.26644	1.2015	119.47	130.59	0.26159
160	2.1185	124.08	135.84	0.27979	1.5750	123.81	135.47	0.27375	1.2488	123.53	135.09	0.26896
180	2.1931	128.16	140.34	0.28693	1.6321	127.91	140.00	0.28095	1.2955	127.66	139.65	0.27621
200	2.2671	132.32	144.91	0.29398	1.6887	132.10	144.60	0.28803	1.3416	131.87	144.28	0.28333
220	2.3408	136.57	149.56	0.30092	1.7449	136.36	149.27	0.29501	1.3873	136.15	148.98	0.29036
240	2.4141	140.89	154.29	0.30778	1.8007	140.70	154.03	0.30190	1.4326	140.50	153.76	0.29728
260	2.4871	145.30	159.10	0.31456	1.8562	145.12	158.86	0.30871	1.4776	144.93	158.60	0.30411
280	2.5598	149.78	163.99	0.32126	1.9114	149.61	163.76	0.31543	1.5223	149.44	163.53	0.31086
	$P = 60$ psia ($T_{sat} = 49.84°F$)				$P = 70$ psia ($T_{sat} = 58.30°F$)				$P = 80$ psia ($T_{sat} = 65.89°F$)			
Sat.	0.7936	101.30	110.11	0.22127	0.6821	102.39	111.22	0.22080	0.59750	103.35	112.20	0.22040
60	0.8179	103.31	112.39	0.22570	0.6857	102.73	111.62	0.22155				
80	0.8636	107.23	116.82	0.23407	0.7271	106.76	116.18	0.23016	0.62430	106.26	115.51	0.22661
100	0.9072	111.16	121.24	0.24211	0.7662	110.76	120.68	0.23836	0.66009	110.34	120.11	0.23499
120	0.9495	115.14	125.68	0.24991	0.8037	114.78	125.19	0.24628	0.69415	114.42	124.69	0.24304
140	0.9908	119.16	130.16	0.25751	0.8401	118.85	129.73	0.25398	0.72698	118.52	129.29	0.25083
160	1.0312	123.25	134.70	0.26496	0.8756	122.97	134.31	0.26149	0.75888	122.68	133.91	0.25841
180	1.0709	127.41	139.30	0.27226	0.9105	127.15	138.94	0.26885	0.79003	126.89	138.58	0.26583
200	1.1101	131.63	143.96	0.27943	0.9447	131.40	143.63	0.27607	0.82059	131.16	143.31	0.27310
220	1.1489	135.93	148.69	0.28649	0.9785	135.71	148.39	0.28317	0.85065	135.49	148.09	0.28024
240	1.1872	140.30	153.48	0.29344	1.0118	140.10	153.21	0.29015	0.88030	139.90	152.93	0.28726
260	1.2252	144.75	158.35	0.30030	1.0449	144.56	158.10	0.29704	0.90961	144.37	157.84	0.29418
280	1.2629	149.27	163.29	0.30707	1.0776	149.10	163.06	0.30384	0.93861	148.92	162.82	0.30100
300	1.3004	153.87	168.31	0.31376	1.1101	153.71	168.09	0.31055	0.96737	153.54	167.86	0.30773
320	1.3377	158.54	173.39	0.32037	1.1424	158.39	173.19	0.31718	0.99590	158.24	172.98	0.31438

Superheated refrigerant-134a (*Concluded*)

R-134a

T °F	v ft³/lbm	u Btu/lbm	h Btu/lbm	s Btu/ lbm · R	v ft³/lbm	u Btu/lbm	h Btu/lbm	s Btu/ lbm · R	v ft³/lbm	u Btu/lbm	h Btu/lbm	s Btu/ lbm · R
	$P = 90$ psia ($T_{sat} = 72.78°F$)				$P = 100$ psia ($T_{sat} = 79.12°F$)				$P = 120$ psia ($T_{sat} = 90.49°F$)			
Sat.	0.53113	104.21	113.06	0.22006	0.47760	104.99	113.83	0.21976	0.39644	106.35	115.16	0.21924
80	0.54388	105.74	114.80	0.22330	0.47906	105.18	114.05	0.22016				
100	0.57729	109.91	119.52	0.23189	0.51076	109.45	118.90	0.22900	0.41013	108.48	117.59	0.22362
120	0.60874	114.04	124.18	0.24008	0.54022	113.66	123.65	0.23733	0.43692	112.84	122.54	0.23232
140	0.63885	118.19	128.83	0.24797	0.56821	117.86	128.37	0.24534	0.46190	117.15	127.41	0.24058
160	0.66796	122.38	133.51	0.25563	0.59513	122.08	133.09	0.25309	0.48563	121.46	132.25	0.24851
180	0.69629	126.62	138.22	0.26311	0.62122	126.35	137.85	0.26063	0.50844	125.79	137.09	0.25619
200	0.72399	130.92	142.97	0.27043	0.64667	130.67	142.64	0.26801	0.53054	130.17	141.95	0.26368
220	0.75119	135.27	147.78	0.27762	0.67158	135.05	147.47	0.27523	0.55206	134.59	146.85	0.27100
240	0.77796	139.69	152.65	0.28468	0.69605	139.49	152.37	0.28233	0.57312	139.07	151.80	0.27817
260	0.80437	144.19	157.58	0.29162	0.72016	143.99	157.32	0.28931	0.59379	143.61	156.79	0.28521
280	0.83048	148.75	162.58	0.29847	0.74396	148.57	162.34	0.29618	0.61413	148.21	161.85	0.29214
300	0.85633	153.38	167.64	0.30522	0.76749	153.21	167.42	0.30296	0.63420	152.88	166.96	0.29896
320	0.88195	158.08	172.77	0.31189	0.79079	157.93	172.56	0.30964	0.65402	157.62	172.14	0.30569
	$P = 140$ psia ($T_{sat} = 100.50°F$)				$P = 160$ psia ($T_{sat} = 109.50°F$)				$P = 180$ psia ($T_{sat} = 117.69°F$)			
Sat.	0.33771	107.51	116.26	0.21879	0.29316	108.50	117.18	0.21836	0.25813	109.36	117.96	0.21795
120	0.36243	111.96	121.35	0.22773	0.30578	111.01	120.06	0.22337	0.26083	109.94	118.63	0.21910
140	0.38551	116.41	126.40	0.23628	0.32774	115.62	125.32	0.23230	0.28231	114.77	124.17	0.22850
160	0.40711	120.81	131.36	0.24443	0.34790	120.13	130.43	0.24069	0.30154	119.42	129.46	0.23718
180	0.42766	125.22	136.30	0.25227	0.36686	124.62	135.49	0.24871	0.31936	124.00	134.64	0.24540
200	0.44743	129.65	141.24	0.25988	0.38494	129.12	140.52	0.25645	0.33619	128.57	139.77	0.25330
220	0.46657	134.12	146.21	0.26730	0.40234	133.64	145.55	0.26397	0.35228	133.15	144.88	0.26094
240	0.48522	138.64	151.21	0.27455	0.41921	138.20	150.62	0.27131	0.36779	137.76	150.01	0.26837
260	0.50345	143.21	156.26	0.28166	0.43564	142.81	155.71	0.27849	0.38284	142.40	155.16	0.27562
280	0.52134	147.85	161.35	0.28864	0.45171	147.48	160.85	0.28554	0.39751	147.10	160.34	0.28273
300	0.53895	152.54	166.50	0.29551	0.46748	152.20	166.04	0.29246	0.41186	151.85	165.57	0.28970
320	0.55630	157.30	171.71	0.30228	0.48299	156.98	171.28	0.29927	0.42594	156.66	170.85	0.29656
340	0.57345	162.13	176.98	0.30896	0.49828	161.83	176.58	0.30598	0.43980	161.53	176.18	0.30331
360	0.59041	167.02	182.32	0.31555	0.51338	166.74	181.94	0.31260	0.45347	166.46	181.56	0.30996
	$P = 200$ psia ($T_{sat} = 125.22°F$)				$P = 300$ psia ($T_{sat} = 156.09°F$)				$P = 400$ psia ($T_{sat} = 179.86°F$)			
Sat.	0.22983	110.11	118.62	0.21753	0.14266	112.60	120.52	0.21512	0.09642	113.35	120.48	0.21161
140	0.24541	113.85	122.93	0.22481								
160	0.26412	118.66	128.44	0.23384	0.14656	113.82	121.95	0.21745				
180	0.28115	123.35	133.76	0.24229	0.16355	119.52	128.60	0.22802	0.09658	113.41	120.56	0.21173
200	0.29704	128.00	138.99	0.25035	0.17776	124.78	134.65	0.23733	0.11440	120.52	128.99	0.22471
220	0.31212	132.64	144.19	0.25812	0.19044	129.85	140.42	0.24594	0.12746	126.44	135.88	0.23500
240	0.32658	137.30	149.38	0.26565	0.20211	134.83	146.05	0.25410	0.13853	131.95	142.20	0.24418
260	0.34054	141.99	154.59	0.27298	0.21306	139.77	151.59	0.26192	0.14844	137.26	148.25	0.25270
280	0.35410	146.72	159.82	0.28015	0.22347	144.70	157.11	0.26947	0.15756	142.48	154.14	0.26077
300	0.36733	151.50	165.09	0.28718	0.23346	149.65	162.61	0.27681	0.16611	147.65	159.94	0.26851
320	0.38029	156.33	170.40	0.29408	0.24310	154.63	168.12	0.28398	0.17423	152.80	165.70	0.27599
340	0.39300	161.22	175.77	0.30087	0.25246	159.64	173.66	0.29098	0.18201	157.97	171.44	0.28326
360	0.40552	166.17	181.18	0.30756	0.26159	164.70	179.22	0.29786	0.18951	163.15	177.18	0.29035

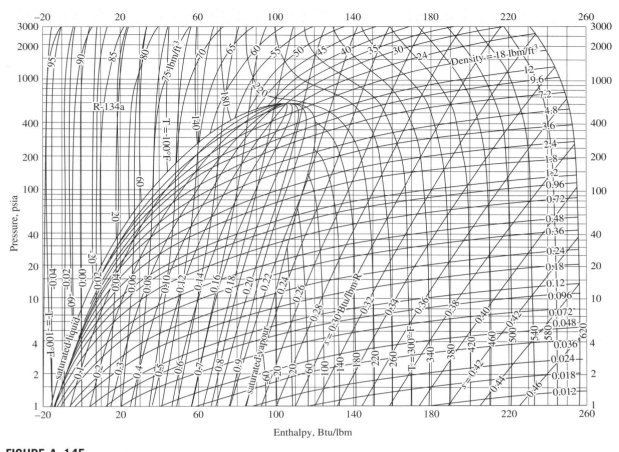

FIGURE A–14E

P-h diagram for refrigerant-134a.

Reprinted by permission of American Society of Heating, Refrigerating, and Air-Conditioning Engineers, Inc., Atlanta, GA.

TABLE A–16E

Properties of the atmosphere at high altitude

Altitude, ft	Temperature, °F	Pressure, psia	Gravity, g, ft/s^2	Speed of sound, ft/s	Density, lbm/ft^3	Viscosity μ, lbm/ft · s	Thermal conductivity, Btu/h · ft · R
0	59.00	14.7	32.174	1116	0.07647	1.202×10^{-5}	0.0146
500	57.22	14.4	32.173	1115	0.07536	1.199×10^{-5}	0.0146
1000	55.43	14.2	32.171	1113	0.07426	1.196×10^{-5}	0.0146
1500	53.65	13.9	32.169	1111	0.07317	1.193×10^{-5}	0.0145
2000	51.87	13.7	32.168	1109	0.07210	1.190×10^{-5}	0.0145
2500	50.09	13.4	32.166	1107	0.07104	1.186×10^{-5}	0.0144
3000	48.30	13.2	32.165	1105	0.06998	1.183×10^{-5}	0.0144
3500	46.52	12.9	32.163	1103	0.06985	1.180×10^{-5}	0.0143
4000	44.74	12.7	32.162	1101	0.06792	1.177×10^{-5}	0.0143
4500	42.96	12.5	32.160	1099	0.06690	1.173×10^{-5}	0.0142
5000	41.17	12.2	32.159	1097	0.06590	1.170×10^{-5}	0.0142
5500	39.39	12.0	32.157	1095	0.06491	1.167×10^{-5}	0.0141
6000	37.61	11.8	32.156	1093	0.06393	1.164×10^{-5}	0.0141
6500	35.83	11.6	32.154	1091	0.06296	1.160×10^{-5}	0.0141
7000	34.05	11.3	32.152	1089	0.06200	1.157×10^{-5}	0.0140
7500	32.26	11.1	32.151	1087	0.06105	1.154×10^{-5}	0.0140
8000	30.48	10.9	32.149	1085	0.06012	1.150×10^{-5}	0.0139
8500	28.70	10.7	32.148	1083	0.05919	1.147×10^{-5}	0.0139
9000	26.92	10.5	32.146	1081	0.05828	1.144×10^{-5}	0.0138
9500	25.14	10.3	32.145	1079	0.05738	1.140×10^{-5}	0.0138
10,000	23.36	10.1	32.145	1077	0.05648	1.137×10^{-5}	0.0137
11,000	19.79	9.72	32.140	1073	0.05473	1.130×10^{-5}	0.0136
12,000	16.23	9.34	32.137	1069	0.05302	1.124×10^{-5}	0.0136
13,000	12.67	8.99	32.134	1065	0.05135	1.117×10^{-5}	0.0135
14,000	9.12	8.63	32.131	1061	0.04973	1.110×10^{-5}	0.0134
15,000	5.55	8.29	32.128	1057	0.04814	1.104×10^{-5}	0.0133
16,000	+1.99	7.97	32.125	1053	0.04659	1.097×10^{-5}	0.0132
17,000	−1.58	7.65	32.122	1049	0.04508	1.090×10^{-5}	0.0132
18,000	−5.14	7.34	32.119	1045	0.04361	1.083×10^{-5}	0.0130
19,000	−8.70	7.05	32.115	1041	0.04217	1.076×10^{-5}	0.0129
20,000	−12.2	6.76	32.112	1037	0.04077	1.070×10^{-5}	0.0128
22,000	−19.4	6.21	32.106	1029	0.03808	1.056×10^{-5}	0.0126
24,000	−26.5	5.70	32.100	1020	0.03553	1.042×10^{-5}	0.0124
26,000	−33.6	5.22	32.094	1012	0.03311	1.028×10^{-5}	0.0122
28,000	−40.7	4.78	32.088	1003	0.03082	1.014×10^{-5}	0.0121
30,000	−47.8	4.37	32.082	995	0.02866	1.000×10^{-5}	0.0119
32,000	−54.9	3.99	32.08	987	0.02661	0.986×10^{-5}	0.0117
34,000	−62.0	3.63	32.07	978	0.02468	0.971×10^{-5}	0.0115
36,000	−69.2	3.30	32.06	969	0.02285	0.956×10^{-5}	0.0113
38,000	−69.7	3.05	32.06	968	0.02079	0.955×10^{-5}	0.0113
40,000	−69.7	2.73	32.05	968	0.01890	0.955×10^{-5}	0.0113
45,000	−69.7	2.148	32.04	968	0.01487	0.955×10^{-5}	0.0113
50,000	−69.7	1.691	32.02	968	0.01171	0.955×10^{-5}	0.0113
55,000	−69.7	1.332	32.00	968	0.00922	0.955×10^{-5}	0.0113
60,000	−69.7	1.048	31.99	968	0.00726	0.955×10^{-5}	0.0113

Source: U.S. Standard Atmosphere Supplements, U.S. Government Printing Office, 1966. Based on year-round mean conditions at 45° latitude and varies with the time of the year and the weather patterns. The conditions at sea level (z = 0) are taken to be P = 14.696 psia, T = 59°F, ρ = 0.076474 lbm/ft^3, g = 32.1741 ft^2/s.

Air

TABLE A–17E

Ideal-gas properties of air

T R	h Btu/lbm	P_r	u Btu/lbm	v_r	s° Btu/lbm·R	T R	h Btu/lbm	P_r	u Btu/lbm	v_r	s° Btu/lbm·R
360	85.97	0.3363	61.29	396.6	0.50369	1600	395.74	71.13	286.06	8.263	0.87130
380	90.75	0.4061	64.70	346.6	0.51663	1650	409.13	80.89	296.03	7.556	0.87954
400	95.53	0.4858	68.11	305.0	0.52890	1700	422.59	90.95	306.06	6.924	0.88758
420	100.32	0.5760	71.52	270.1	0.54058	1750	436.12	101.98	316.16	6.357	0.89542
440	105.11	0.6776	74.93	240.6	0.55172	1800	449.71	114.0	326.32	5.847	0.90308
460	109.90	0.7913	78.36	215.33	0.56235	1850	463.37	127.2	336.55	5.388	0.91056
480	114.69	0.9182	81.77	193.65	0.57255	1900	477.09	141.5	346.85	4.974	0.91788
500	119.48	1.0590	85.20	174.90	0.58233	1950	490.88	157.1	357.20	4.598	0.92504
520	124.27	1.2147	88.62	158.58	0.59173	2000	504.71	174.0	367.61	4.258	0.93205
537	128.10	1.3593	91.53	146.34	0.59945	2050	518.71	192.3	378.08	3.949	0.93891
540	129.06	1.3860	92.04	144.32	0.60078	2100	532.55	212.1	388.60	3.667	0.94564
560	133.86	1.5742	95.47	131.78	0.60950	2150	546.54	223.5	399.17	3.410	0.95222
580	138.66	1.7800	98.90	120.70	0.61793	2200	560.59	256.6	409.78	3.176	0.95919
600	143.47	2.005	102.34	110.88	0.62607	2250	574.69	281.4	420.46	2.961	0.96501
620	148.28	2.249	105.78	102.12	0.63395	2300	588.82	308.1	431.16	2.765	0.97123
640	153.09	2.514	109.21	94.30	0.64159	2350	603.00	336.8	441.91	2.585	0.97732
660	157.92	2.801	112.67	87.27	0.64902	2400	617.22	367.6	452.70	2.419	0.98331
680	162.73	3.111	116.12	80.96	0.65621	2450	631.48	400.5	463.54	2.266	0.98919
700	167.56	3.446	119.58	75.25	0.66321	2500	645.78	435.7	474.40	2.125	0.99497
720	172.39	3.806	123.04	70.07	0.67002	2550	660.12	473.3	485.31	1.996	1.00064
740	177.23	4.193	126.51	65.38	0.67665	2600	674.49	513.5	496.26	1.876	1.00623
760	182.08	4.607	129.99	61.10	0.68312	2650	688.90	556.3	507.25	1.765	1.01172
780	186.94	5.051	133.47	57.20	0.68942	2700	703.35	601.9	518.26	1.662	1.01712
800	191.81	5.526	136.97	53.63	0.69558	2750	717.83	650.4	529.31	1.566	1.02244
820	196.69	6.033	140.47	50.35	0.70160	2800	732.33	702.0	540.40	1.478	1.02767
840	201.56	6.573	143.98	47.34	0.70747	2850	746.88	756.7	551.52	1.395	1.03282
860	206.46	7.149	147.50	44.57	0.71323	2900	761.45	814.8	562.66	1.318	1.03788
880	211.35	7.761	151.02	42.01	0.71886	2950	776.05	876.4	573.84	1.247	1.04288
900	216.26	8.411	154.57	39.64	0.72438	3000	790.68	941.4	585.04	1.180	1.04779
920	221.18	9.102	158.12	37.44	0.72979	3050	805.34	1011	596.28	1.118	1.05264
940	226.11	9.834	161.68	35.41	0.73509	3100	820.03	1083	607.53	1.060	1.05741
960	231.06	10.61	165.26	33.52	0.74030	3150	834.75	1161	618.82	1.006	1.06212
980	236.02	11.43	168.83	31.76	0.74540	3200	849.48	1242	630.12	0.955	1.06676
1000	240.98	12.30	172.43	30.12	0.75042	3250	864.24	1328	641.46	0.907	1.07134
1040	250.95	14.18	179.66	27.17	0.76019	3300	879.02	1418	652.81	0.8621	1.07585
1080	260.97	16.28	186.93	24.58	0.76964	3350	893.83	1513	664.20	0.8202	1.08031
1120	271.03	18.60	194.25	22.30	0.77880	3400	908.66	1613	675.60	0.7807	1.08470
1160	281.14	21.18	201.63	20.29	0.78767	3450	923.52	1719	687.04	0.7436	1.08904
1200	291.30	24.01	209.05	18.51	0.79628	3500	938.40	1829	698.48	0.7087	1.09332
1240	301.52	27.13	216.53	16.93	0.80466	3550	953.30	1946	709.95	0.6759	1.09755
1280	311.79	30.55	224.05	15.52	0.81280	3600	968.21	2068	721.44	0.6449	1.10172
1320	322.11	34.31	231.63	14.25	0.82075	3650	983.15	2196	732.95	0.6157	1.10584
1360	332.48	38.41	239.25	13.12	0.82848	3700	998.11	2330	744.48	0.5882	1.10991
1400	342.90	42.88	246.93	12.10	0.83604	3750	1013.1	2471	756.04	0.5621	1.11393
1440	353.37	47.75	254.66	11.17	0.84341	3800	1028.1	2618	767.60	0.5376	1.11791
1480	363.89	53.04	262.44	10.34	0.85062	3850	1043.1	2773	779.19	0.5143	1.12183
1520	374.47	58.78	270.26	9.578	0.85767	3900	1058.1	2934	790.80	0.4923	1.12571
1560	385.08	65.00	278.13	8.890	0.86456	3950	1073.2	3103	802.43	0.4715	1.12955

Air

Ideal-gas properties of air (*Concluded*)

T R	h Btu/lbm	P_r	u Btu/lbm	v_r	$s°$ Btu/lbm · R	T R	h Btu/lbm	P_r	u Btu/lbm	v_r	$s°$ Btu/lbm · R
4000	1088.3	3280	814.06	0.4518	1.13334	4600	1270.4	6089	955.04	0.2799	1.17575
4050	1103.4	3464	825.72	0.4331	1.13709	4700	1300.9	6701	978.73	0.2598	1.18232
4100	1118.5	3656	837.40	0.4154	1.14079	4800	1331.5	7362	1002.5	0.2415	1.18876
4150	1133.6	3858	849.09	0.3985	1.14446	4900	1362.2	8073	1026.3	0.2248	1.19508
4200	1148.7	4067	860.81	0.3826	1.14809	5000	1392.9	8837	1050.1	0.2096	1.20129
4300	1179.0	4513	884.28	0.3529	1.15522	5100	1423.6	9658	1074.0	0.1956	1.20738
4400	1209.4	4997	907.81	0.3262	1.16221	5200	1454.4	10,539	1098.0	0.1828	1.21336
4500	1239.9	5521	931.39	0.3019	1.16905	5300	1485.3	11,481	1122.0	0.1710	1.21923

Note: The properties P_r (relative pressure) and v_r (relative specific volume) are dimensionless quantities used in the analysis of isentropic processes, and should not be confused with the properties pressure and specific volume.

Source: Kenneth Wark, *Thermodynamics*, 4th ed. (New York: McGraw-Hill, 1983), pp. 832–33, Table A–5. Originally published in J. H. Keenan and J. Kaye, *Gas Tables* (New York: John Wiley & Sons, 1948).

Air

TABLE A–18E

Ideal-gas properties of nitrogen, N_2

T R	$\bar{h}$ Btu/lbmol	$\bar{u}$ Btu/lbmol	$\bar{s}°$ Btu/lbmol·R	T R	$\bar{h}$ Btu/lbmol	$\bar{u}$ Btu/lbmol	$\bar{s}°$ Btu/lbmol·R
300	2,082.0	1,486.2	41.695	1080	7,551.0	5,406.2	50.651
320	2,221.0	1,585.5	42.143	1100	7,695.0	5,510.5	50.783
340	2,360.0	1,684.4	42.564	1120	7,839.3	5,615.2	50.912
360	2,498.9	1,784.0	42.962	1140	7,984.0	5,720.1	51.040
380	2,638.0	1,883.4	43.337	1160	8,129.0	5,825.4	51.167
400	2,777.0	1,982.6	43.694	1180	8,274.4	5,931.0	51.291
420	2,916.1	2,082.0	44.034	1200	8,420.0	6,037.0	51.143
440	3,055.1	2,181.3	44.357	1220	8,566.1	6,143.4	51.534
460	3,194.1	2,280.6	44.665	1240	8,712.6	6,250.1	51.653
480	3,333.1	2,379.9	44.962	1260	8,859.3	6,357.2	51.771
500	3,472.2	2,479.3	45.246	1280	9,006.4	6,464.5	51.887
520	3,611.3	2,578.6	45.519	1300	9,153.9	6,572.3	51.001
537	3,729.5	2,663.1	45.743	1320	9,301.8	6,680.4	52.114
540	3,750.3	2,678.0	45.781	1340	9,450.0	6,788.9	52.225
560	3,889.5	2,777.4	46.034	1360	9,598.6	6,897.8	52.335
580	4,028.7	2,876.9	46.278	1380	9,747.5	7,007.0	52.444
600	4,167.9	2,976.4	46.514	1400	9,896.9	7,116.7	52.551
620	4,307.1	3,075.9	46.742	1420	10,046.6	7,226.7	52.658
640	4,446.4	3,175.5	46.964	1440	10,196.6	7,337.0	52.763
660	4,585.8	3,275.2	47.178	1460	10,347.0	7,447.6	52.867
680	4,725.3	3,374.9	47.386	1480	10,497.8	7,558.7	52.969
700	4,864.9	3,474.8	47.588	1500	10,648.0	7,670.1	53.071
720	5,004.5	3,574.7	47.785	1520	10,800.4	7,781.9	53.171
740	5,144.3	3,674.7	47.977	1540	10,952.2	7,893.9	53.271
760	5,284.1	3,774.9	48.164	1560	11,104.3	8,006.4	53.369
780	5,424.2	3,875.2	48.345	1580	11,256.9	8,119.2	53.465
800	5,564.4	3,975.7	48.522	1600	11,409.7	8,232.3	53.561
820	5,704.7	4,076.3	48.696	1620	11,562.8	8,345.7	53.656
840	5,845.3	4,177.1	48.865	1640	11,716.4	8,459.6	53.751
860	5,985.9	4,278.1	49.031	1660	11,870.2	8,573.6	53.844
880	6,126.9	4,379.4	49.193	1680	12,024.3	8,688.1	53.936
900	6,268.1	4,480.8	49.352	1700	12,178.9	8,802.9	54.028
920	6,409.6	4,582.6	49.507	1720	12,333.7	8,918.0	54.118
940	6,551.2	4,684.5	49.659	1740	12,488.8	9,033.4	54.208
960	6,693.1	4,786.7	49.808	1760	12,644.3	9,149.2	54.297
980	6,835.4	4,889.3	49.955	1780	12,800.2	9,265.3	54.385
1000	6,977.9	4,992.0	50.099	1800	12,956.3	9,381.7	54.472
1020	7,120.7	5,095.1	50.241	1820	13,112.7	9,498.4	54.559
1040	7,263.8	5,198.5	50.380	1840	13,269.5	9,615.5	54.645
1060	7,407.2	5,302.2	50.516	1860	13,426.5	9,732.8	54.729

N_2

TABLE A–18E

Ideal-gas properties of nitrogen, N_2 (*Concluded*)

T R	$\bar{h}$ Btu/lbmol	$\bar{u}$ Btu/lbmol	$\bar{s}°$ Btu/lbmol·R	T R	$\bar{h}$ Btu/lbmol	$\bar{u}$ Btu/lbmol	$\bar{s}°$ Btu/lbmol·R
1900	13,742	9,968	54.896	3500	27,016	20,065	59.944
1940	14,058	10,205	55.061	3540	27,359	20,329	60.041
1980	14,375	10,443	55.223	3580	27,703	20,593	60.138
2020	14,694	10,682	55.383	3620	28,046	20,858	60.234
2060	15,013	10,923	55.540	3660	28,391	21,122	60.328
2100	15,334	11,164	55.694	3700	28,735	21,387	60.422
2140	15,656	11,406	55.846	3740	29,080	21,653	60.515
2180	15,978	11,649	55.995	3780	29,425	21,919	60.607
2220	16,302	11,893	56.141	3820	29,771	22,185	60.698
2260	16,626	12,138	56.286	3860	30,117	22,451	60.788
2300	16,951	12,384	56.429	3900	30,463	22,718	60.877
2340	17,277	12,630	56.570	3940	30,809	22,985	60.966
2380	17,604	12,878	56.708	3980	31,156	23,252	61.053
2420	17,392	13,126	56.845	4020	31,503	23,520	61.139
2460	18,260	13,375	56.980	4060	31,850	23,788	61.225
2500	18,590	13,625	57.112	4100	32,198	24,056	61.310
2540	18,919	13,875	57.243	4140	32,546	24,324	61.395
2580	19,250	14,127	57.372	4180	32,894	24,593	61.479
2620	19,582	14,379	57.499	4220	33,242	24,862	61.562
2660	19,914	14,631	57.625	4260	33,591	25,131	61.644
2700	20,246	14,885	57.750	4300	33,940	25,401	61.726
2740	20,580	15,139	57.872	4340	34,289	25,670	61.806
2780	20,914	15,393	57.993	4380	34,638	25,940	61.887
2820	21,248	15,648	58.113	4420	34,988	26,210	61.966
2860	21,584	15,905	58.231	4460	35,338	26,481	62.045
2900	21,920	16,161	58.348	4500	35,688	26,751	62.123
2940	22,256	16,417	58.463	4540	36,038	27,022	62.201
2980	22,593	16,675	58.576	4580	36,389	27,293	62.278
3020	22,930	16,933	58.688	4620	36,739	27,565	62.354
3060	23,268	17,192	58.800	4660	37,090	27,836	62.429
3100	23,607	17,451	58.910	4700	37,441	28,108	62.504
3140	23,946	17,710	59.019	4740	37,792	28,379	62.578
3180	24,285	17,970	59.126	4780	38,144	28,651	62.652
3220	24,625	18,231	59.232	4820	38,495	28,924	62.725
3260	24,965	18,491	59.338	4860	38,847	29,196	62.798
3300	25,306	18,753	59.442	4900	39,199	29,468	62.870
3340	25,647	19,014	59.544	5000	40,080	30,151	63.049
3380	25,989	19,277	59.646	5100	40,962	30,834	63.223
3420	26,331	19,539	59.747	5200	41,844	31,518	63.395
3460	26,673	19,802	59.846	5300	42,728	32,203	63.563

Source: Tables A–18E through A–23E are adapted from Kenneth Wark, *Thermodynamics*, 4th ed. (New York: McGraw-Hill, 1983), pp. 834–44. Originally published in J. H. Keenan and J. Kaye, *Gas Tables* (New York: John Wiley & Sons, 1945).

TABLE A–19E

Ideal-gas properties of oxygen, O_2

T R	$\bar{h}$ Btu/lbmol	$\bar{u}$ Btu/lbmol	$\bar{s}°$ Btu/lbmol·R	T R	$\bar{h}$ Btu/lbmol	$\bar{u}$ Btu/lbmol	$\bar{s}°$ Btu/lbmol·R
300	2,073.5	1,477.8	44.927	1080	7,696.8	5,552.1	54.064
320	2,212.6	1,577.1	45.375	1100	7,850.4	5,665.9	54.204
340	2,351.7	1,676.5	45.797	1120	8,004.5	5,780.3	54.343
360	2,490.8	1,775.9	46.195	1140	8,159.1	5,895.2	54.480
380	2,630.0	1,875.3	46.571	1160	8,314.2	6,010.6	54.614
400	2,769.1	1,974.8	46.927	1180	8,469.8	6,126.5	54.748
420	2,908.3	2,074.3	47.267	1200	8,625.8	6,242.8	54.879
440	3,047.5	2,173.8	47.591	1220	8,782.4	6,359.6	55.008
460	3,186.9	2,273.4	47.900	1240	8,939.4	6,476.9	55.136
480	3,326.5	2,373.3	48.198	1260	9,096.7	6,594.5	55.262
500	3,466.2	2,473.2	48.483	1280	9,254.6	6,712.7	55.386
520	3,606.1	2,573.4	48.757	1300	9,412.9	6,831.3	55.508
537	3,725.1	2,658.7	48.982	1320	9,571.9	6,950.2	55.630
540	3,746.2	2,673.8	49.021	1340	9,730.7	7,069.6	55.750
560	3,886.6	2,774.5	49.276	1360	9,890.2	7,189.4	55.867
580	4,027.3	2,875.5	49.522	1380	10,050.1	7,309.6	55.984
600	4,168.3	2,976.8	49.762	1400	10,210.4	7,430.1	56.099
620	4,309.7	3,078.4	49.993	1420	10,371.0	7,551.1	56.213
640	4,451.4	3,180.4	50.218	1440	10,532.0	7,672.4	56.326
660	4,593.5	3,282.9	50.437	1460	10,693.3	7,793.9	56.437
680	4,736.2	3,385.8	50.650	1480	10,855.1	7,916.0	56.547
700	4,879.3	3,489.2	50.858	1500	11,017.1	8,038.3	56.656
720	5,022.9	3,593.1	51.059	1520	11,179.6	8,161.1	56.763
740	5,167.0	3,697.4	51.257	1540	11,342.4	8,284.2	56.869
760	5,311.4	3,802.4	51.450	1560	11,505.4	8,407.4	56.975
780	5,456.4	3,907.5	51.638	1580	11,668.8	8,531.1	57.079
800	5,602.0	4,013.3	51.821	1600	11,832.5	8,655.1	57.182
820	5,748.1	4,119.7	52.002	1620	11,996.6	8,779.5	57.284
840	5,894.8	4,226.6	52.179	1640	12,160.9	8,904.1	57.385
860	6,041.9	4,334.1	52.352	1660	12,325.5	9,029.0	57.484
880	6,189.6	4,442.0	52.522	1680	12,490.4	9,154.1	57.582
900	6,337.9	4,550.6	52.688	1700	12,655.6	9,279.6	57.680
920	6,486.7	4,659.7	52.852	1720	12,821.1	9,405.4	57.777
940	6,636.1	4,769.4	53.012	1740	12,986.9	9,531.5	57.873
960	6,786.0	4,879.5	53.170	1760	13,153.0	9,657.9	57.968
980	6,936.4	4,990.3	53.326	1780	13,319.2	9,784.4	58.062
1000	7,087.5	5,101.6	53.477	1800	13,485.8	9,911.2	58.155
1020	7,238.9	5,213.3	53.628	1820	13,652.5	10,038.2	58.247
1040	7,391.0	5,325.7	53.775	1840	13,819.6	10,165.6	58.339
1060	7,543.6	5,438.6	53.921	1860	13,986.8	10,293.1	58.428

O_2

TABLE A–19E

Ideal-gas properties of oxygen, O_2 (*Concluded*)

T R	$\bar{h}$ Btu/lbmol	$\bar{u}$ Btu/lbmol	$\bar{s}°$ Btu/lbmol·R	T R	$\bar{h}$ Btu/lbmol	$\bar{u}$ Btu/lbmol	$\bar{s}°$ Btu/lbmol·R
1900	14,322	10,549	58.607	3500	28,273	21,323	63.914
1940	14,658	10,806	58.782	3540	28,633	21,603	64.016
1980	14,995	11,063	58.954	3580	28,994	21,884	64.114
2020	15,333	11,321	59.123	3620	29,354	22,165	64.217
2060	15,672	11,581	59.289	3660	29,716	22,447	64.316
2100	16,011	11,841	59.451	3700	30,078	22,730	64.415
2140	16,351	12,101	59.612	3740	30,440	23,013	64.512
2180	16,692	12,363	59.770	3780	30,803	23,296	64.609
2220	17,036	12,625	59.926	3820	31,166	23,580	64.704
2260	17,376	12,888	60.077	3860	31,529	23,864	64.800
2300	17,719	13,151	60.228	3900	31,894	24,149	64.893
2340	18,062	13,416	60.376	3940	32,258	24,434	64.986
2380	18,407	13,680	60.522	3980	32,623	24,720	65.078
2420	18,572	13,946	60.666	4020	32,989	25,006	65.169
2460	19,097	14,212	60.808	4060	33,355	25,292	65.260
2500	19,443	14,479	60.946	4100	33,722	25,580	65.350
2540	19,790	14,746	61.084	4140	34,089	25,867	64.439
2580	20,138	15,014	61.220	4180	34,456	26,155	65.527
2620	20,485	15,282	61.354	4220	34,824	26,144	65.615
2660	20,834	15,551	61.486	4260	35,192	26,733	65.702
2700	21,183	15,821	61.616	4300	35,561	27,022	65.788
2740	21,533	16,091	61.744	4340	35,930	27,312	65.873
2780	21,883	16,362	61.871	4380	36,300	27,602	65.958
2820	22,232	16,633	61.996	4420	36,670	27,823	66.042
2860	22,584	16,905	62.120	4460	37,041	28,184	66.125
2900	22,936	17,177	62.242	4500	37,412	28,475	66.208
2940	23,288	17,450	62.363	4540	37,783	28,768	66.290
2980	23,641	17,723	62.483	4580	38,155	29,060	66.372
3020	23,994	17,997	62.599	4620	38,528	29,353	66.453
3060	24,348	18,271	62.716	4660	38,900	29,646	66.533
3100	24,703	18,546	62.831	4700	39,274	29,940	66.613
3140	25,057	18,822	62.945	4740	39,647	30,234	66.691
3180	25,413	19,098	63.057	4780	40,021	30,529	66.770
3220	25,769	19,374	63.169	4820	40,396	30,824	66.848
3260	26,175	19,651	63.279	4860	40,771	31,120	66.925
3300	26,412	19,928	63.386	4900	41,146	31,415	67.003
3340	26,839	20,206	63.494	5000	42,086	32,157	67.193
3380	27,197	20,485	63.601	5100	43,021	32,901	67.380
3420	27,555	20,763	63.706	5200	43,974	33,648	67.562
3460	27,914	21,043	63.811	5300	44,922	34,397	67.743

O_2

Ideal-gas properties of carbon dioxide, CO_2

T R	$\bar{h}$ Btu/lbmol	$\bar{u}$ Btu/lbmol	$\bar{s}°$ Btu/lbmol·R	T R	$\bar{h}$ Btu/lbmol	$\bar{u}$ Btu/lbmol	$\bar{s}°$ Btu/lbmol·R
300	2,108.2	1,512.4	46.353	1080	9,575.8	7,431.1	58.072
320	2,256.6	1,621.1	46.832	1100	9,802.6	7,618.1	58.281
340	2,407.3	1,732.1	47.289	1120	10,030.6	7,806.4	58.485
360	2,560.5	1,845.6	47.728	1140	10,260.1	7,996.2	58.689
380	2,716.4	1,961.8	48.148	1160	10,490.6	8,187.0	58.889
400	2,874.7	2,080.4	48.555	1180	10,722.3	8,379.0	59.088
420	3,035.7	2,201.7	48.947	1200	10,955.3	8,572.3	59.283
440	3,199.4	2,325.6	49.329	1220	11,189.4	8,766.6	59.477
460	3,365.7	2,452.2	49.698	1240	11,424.6	8,962.1	59.668
480	3,534.7	2,581.5	50.058	1260	11,661.0	9,158.8	59.858
500	3,706.2	2,713.3	50.408	1280	11,898.4	9,356.5	60.044
520	3,880.3	2,847.7	50.750	1300	12,136.9	9,555.3	60.229
537	4,027.5	2,963.8	51.032	1320	12,376.4	9,755.0	60.412
540	4,056.8	2,984.4	51.082	1340	12,617.0	9,955.9	60.593
560	4,235.8	3,123.7	51.408	1360	12,858.5	10,157.7	60.772
580	4,417.2	3,265.4	51.726	1380	13,101.0	10,360.5	60.949
600	4,600.9	3,409.4	52.038	1400	13,344.7	10,564.5	61.124
620	4,786.6	3,555.6	52.343	1420	13,589.1	10,769.2	61.298
640	4,974.9	3,704.0	52.641	1440	13,834.5	10,974.8	61.469
660	5,165.2	3,854.6	52.934	1460	14,080.8	11,181.4	61.639
680	5,357.6	4,007.2	53.225	1480	14,328.0	11,388.9	61.800
700	5,552.0	4,161.9	53.503	1500	14,576.0	11,597.2	61.974
720	5,748.4	4,318.6	53.780	1520	14,824.9	11,806.4	62.138
740	5,946.8	4,477.3	54.051	1540	15,074.7	12,016.5	62.302
760	6,147.0	4,637.9	54.319	1560	15,325.3	12,227.3	62.464
780	6,349.1	4,800.1	54.582	1580	15,576.7	12,439.0	62.624
800	6,552.9	4,964.2	54.839	1600	15,829.0	12,651.6	62.783
820	6,758.3	5,129.9	55.093	1620	16,081.9	12,864.8	62.939
840	6,965.7	5,297.6	55.343	1640	16,335.7	13,078.9	63.095
860	7,174.7	5,466.9	55.589	1660	16,590.2	13,293.7	63.250
880	7,385.3	5,637.7	55.831	1680	16,845.5	13,509.2	63.403
900	7,597.6	5,810.3	56.070	1700	17,101.4	13,725.4	63.555
920	7,811.4	5,984.4	56.305	1720	17,358.1	13,942.4	63.704
940	8,026.8	6,160.1	56.536	1740	17,615.5	14,160.1	63.853
960	8,243.8	6,337.4	56.765	1760	17,873.5	14,378.4	64.001
980	8,462.2	6,516.1	56.990	1780	18,132.2	14,597.4	64.147
1000	8,682.1	6,696.2	57.212	1800	18,391.5	14,816.9	64.292
1020	8,903.4	6,877.8	57.432	1820	18,651.5	15,037.2	64.435
1040	9,126.2	7,060.9	57.647	1840	18,912.2	15,258.2	64.578
1060	9,350.3	7,245.3	57.861	1860	19,173.4	15,479.7	64.719

CO_2

Ideal-gas properties of carbon dioxide, CO_2 (*Concluded*)

T R	$\bar{h}$ Btu/lbmol	$\bar{u}$ Btu/lbmol	$\bar{s}°$ Btu/lbmol·R	T R	$\bar{h}$ Btu/lbmol	$\bar{u}$ Btu/lbmol	$\bar{s}°$ Btu/lbmol·R
1900	19,698	15,925	64.999	3500	41,965	35,015	73.462
1940	20,224	16,372	65.272	3540	42,543	35,513	73.627
1980	20,753	16,821	65.543	3580	43,121	36,012	73.789
2020	21,284	17,273	65.809	3620	43,701	36,512	73.951
2060	21,818	17,727	66.069	3660	44,280	37,012	74.110
2100	22,353	18,182	66.327	3700	44,861	37,513	74.267
2140	22,890	18,640	66.581	3740	45,442	38,014	74.423
2180	23,429	19,101	66.830	3780	46,023	38,517	74.578
2220	23,970	19,561	67.076	3820	46,605	39,019	74.732
2260	24,512	20,024	67.319	3860	47,188	39,522	74.884
2300	25,056	20,489	67.557	3900	47,771	40,026	75.033
2340	25,602	20,955	67.792	3940	48,355	40,531	75.182
2380	26,150	21,423	68.025	3980	48,939	41,035	75.330
2420	26,699	21,893	68.253	4020	49,524	41,541	75.477
2460	27,249	22,364	68.479	4060	50,109	42,047	75.622
2500	27,801	22,837	68.702	4100	50,695	42,553	75.765
2540	28,355	23,310	68.921	4140	51,282	43,060	75.907
2580	28,910	23,786	69.138	4180	51,868	43,568	76.048
2620	29,465	24,262	69.352	4220	52,456	44,075	76.188
2660	30,023	24,740	69.563	4260	53,044	44,584	76.327
2700	30,581	25,220	69.771	4300	53,632	45,093	76.464
2740	31,141	25,701	69.977	4340	54,221	45,602	76.601
2780	31,702	26,181	70.181	4380	54,810	46,112	76.736
2820	32,264	26,664	70.382	4420	55,400	46,622	76.870
2860	32,827	27,148	70.580	4460	55,990	47,133	77.003
2900	33,392	27,633	70.776	4500	56,581	47,645	77.135
2940	33,957	28,118	70.970	4540	57,172	48,156	77.266
2980	34,523	28,605	71.160	4580	57,764	48,668	77.395
3020	35,090	29,093	71.350	4620	58,356	49,181	77.581
3060	35,659	29,582	71.537	4660	58,948	49,694	77.652
3100	36,228	30,072	71.722	4700	59,541	50,208	77.779
3140	36,798	30,562	71.904	4740	60,134	50,721	77.905
3180	37,369	31,054	72.085	4780	60,728	51,236	78.029
3220	37,941	31,546	72.264	4820	61,322	51,750	78.153
3260	38,513	32,039	72.441	4860	61,916	52,265	78.276
3300	39,087	32,533	72.616	4900	62,511	52,781	78.398
3340	39,661	33,028	72.788	5000	64,000	54,071	78.698
3380	40,236	33,524	72.960	5100	65,491	55,363	78.994
3420	40,812	34,020	73.129	5200	66,984	56,658	79.284
3460	41,388	34,517	73.297	5300	68,471	57,954	79.569

CO_2

TABLE A–21E

Ideal-gas properties of carbon monoxide, CO

T R	$\bar{h}$ Btu/lbmol	$\bar{u}$ Btu/lbmol	$\bar{s}°$ Btu/lbmol·R	T R	$\bar{h}$ Btu/lbmol	$\bar{u}$ Btu/lbmol	$\bar{s}°$ Btu/lbmol·R
300	2,081.9	1,486.1	43.223	1080	7,571.1	5,426.4	52.203
320	2,220.9	1,585.4	43.672	1100	7,716.8	5,532.3	52.337
340	2,359.9	1,684.7	44.093	1120	7,862.9	5,638.7	52.468
360	2,498.8	1,783.9	44.490	1140	8,009.2	5,745.4	52.598
380	2,637.9	1,883.3	44.866	1160	8,156.1	5,851.5	52.726
400	2,776.9	1,982.6	45.223	1180	8,303.3	5,960.0	52.852
420	2,916.0	2,081.9	45.563	1200	8,450.8	6,067.8	52.976
440	3,055.0	2,181.2	45.886	1220	8,598.8	6,176.0	53.098
460	3,194.0	2,280.5	46.194	1240	8,747.2	6,284.7	53.218
480	3,333.0	2,379.8	46.491	1260	8,896.0	6,393.8	53.337
500	3,472.1	2,479.2	46.775	1280	9,045.0	6,503.1	53.455
520	3,611.2	2,578.6	47.048	1300	9,194.6	6,613.0	53.571
537	3,725.1	2,663.1	47.272	1320	9,344.6	6,723.2	53.685
540	3,750.3	2,677.9	47.310	1340	9,494.8	6,833.7	53.799
560	3,889.5	2,777.4	47.563	1360	9,645.5	6,944.7	53.910
580	4,028.7	2,876.9	47.807	1380	9,796.6	7,056.1	54.021
600	4,168.0	2,976.5	48.044	1400	9,948.1	7,167.9	54.129
620	4,307.4	3,076.2	48.272	1420	10,100.0	7,280.1	54.237
640	4,446.9	3,175.9	48.494	1440	10,252.2	7,392.6	54.344
660	4,586.6	3,275.8	48.709	1460	10,404.8	7,505.4	54.448
680	4,726.2	3,375.8	48.917	1480	10,557.8	7,618.7	54.522
700	4,886.0	3,475.9	49.120	1500	10,711.1	7,732.3	54.665
720	5,006.1	3,576.3	49.317	1520	10,864.9	7,846.4	54.757
740	5,146.4	3,676.9	49.509	1540	11,019.0	7,960.8	54.858
760	5,286.8	3,777.5	49.697	1560	11,173.4	8,075.4	54.958
780	5,427.4	3,878.4	49.880	1580	11,328.2	8,190.5	55.056
800	5,568.2	3,979.5	50.058	1600	11,483.4	8,306.0	55.154
820	5,709.4	4,081.0	50.232	1620	11,638.9	8,421.8	55.251
840	5,850.7	4,182.6	50.402	1640	11,794.7	8,537.9	55.347
860	5,992.3	4,284.5	50.569	1660	11,950.9	8,654.4	55.411
880	6,134.2	4,386.6	50.732	1680	12,107.5	8,771.2	55.535
900	6,276.4	4,489.1	50.892	1700	12,264.3	8,888.3	55.628
920	6,419.0	4,592.0	51.048	1720	12,421.4	9,005.7	55.720
940	6,561.7	4,695.0	51.202	1740	12,579.0	9,123.6	55.811
960	6,704.9	4,798.5	51.353	1760	12,736.7	9,241.6	55.900
980	6,848.4	4,902.3	51.501	1780	12,894.9	9,360.0	55.990
1000	6,992.2	5,006.3	51.646	1800	13,053.2	9,478.6	56.078
1020	7,136.4	5,110.8	51.788	1820	13,212.0	9,597.7	56.166
1040	7,281.0	5,215.7	51.929	1840	13,371.0	9,717.0	56.253
1060	7,425.9	5,320.9	52.067	1860	13,530.2	9,836.5	56.339

CO

TABLE A–21E

Ideal-gas properties of carbon monoxide, CO (*Concluded*)

T R	$\bar{h}$ Btu/lbmol	$\bar{u}$ Btu/lbmol	$\bar{s}°$ Btu/lbmol·R	T R	$\bar{h}$ Btu/lbmol	$\bar{u}$ Btu/lbmol	$\bar{s}°$ Btu/lbmol·R
1900	13,850	10,077	56.509	3500	27,262	20,311	61.612
1940	14,170	10,318	56.677	3540	27,608	20,576	61.710
1980	14,492	10,560	56.841	3580	27,954	20,844	61.807
2020	14,815	10,803	57.007	3620	28,300	21,111	61.903
2060	15,139	11,048	57.161	3660	28,647	21,378	61.998
2100	15,463	11,293	57.317	3700	28,994	21,646	62.093
2140	15,789	11,539	57.470	3740	29,341	21,914	62.186
2180	16,116	11,787	57.621	3780	29,688	22,182	62.279
2220	16,443	12,035	57.770	3820	30,036	22,450	62.370
2260	16,722	12,284	57.917	3860	30,384	22,719	62.461
2300	17,101	12,534	58.062	3900	30,733	22,988	62.511
2340	17,431	12,784	58.204	3940	31,082	23,257	62.640
2380	17,762	13,035	58.344	3980	31,431	23,527	62.728
2420	18,093	13,287	58.482	4020	31,780	23,797	62.816
2460	18,426	13,541	58.619	4060	32,129	24,067	62.902
2500	18,759	13,794	58.754	4100	32,479	24,337	62.988
2540	19,093	14,048	58.885	4140	32,829	24,608	63.072
2580	19,427	14,303	59.016	4180	33,179	24,878	63.156
2620	19,762	14,559	59.145	4220	33,530	25,149	63.240
2660	20,098	14,815	59.272	4260	33,880	25,421	63.323
2700	20,434	15,072	59.398	4300	34,231	25,692	63.405
2740	20,771	15,330	59.521	4340	34,582	25,934	63.486
2780	21,108	15,588	59.644	4380	34,934	26,235	63.567
2820	21,446	15,846	59.765	4420	35,285	26,508	63.647
2860	21,785	16,105	59.884	4460	35,637	26,780	63.726
2900	22,124	16,365	60.002	4500	35,989	27,052	63.805
2940	22,463	16,225	60.118	4540	36,341	27,325	63.883
2980	22,803	16,885	60.232	4580	36,693	27,598	63.960
3020	23,144	17,146	60.346	4620	37,046	27,871	64.036
3060	23,485	17,408	60.458	4660	37,398	28,144	64.113
3100	23,826	17,670	60.569	4700	37,751	28,417	64.188
3140	24,168	17,932	60.679	4740	38,104	28,691	64.263
3180	24,510	18,195	60.787	4780	38,457	28,965	64.337
3220	24,853	18,458	60.894	4820	38,811	29,239	64.411
3260	25,196	18,722	61.000	4860	39,164	29,513	64.484
3300	25,539	18,986	61.105	4900	39,518	29,787	64.556
3340	25,883	19,250	61.209	5000	40,403	30,473	64.735
3380	26,227	19,515	61.311	5100	41,289	31,161	64.910
3420	26,572	19,780	61.412	5200	42,176	31,849	65.082
3460	26,917	20,045	61.513	5300	43,063	32,538	65.252

CO

TABLE A–22E

Ideal-gas properties of hydrogen, H_2

T R	$\bar{h}$ Btu/lbmol	$\bar{u}$ Btu/lbmol	$\bar{s}°$ Btu/lbmol · R	T R	$\bar{h}$ Btu/lbmol	$\bar{u}$ Btu/lbmol	$\bar{s}°$ Btu/lbmol · R
300	2,063.5	1,467.7	27.337	1400	9,673.8	6,893.6	37.883
320	2,189.4	1,553.9	27.742	1500	10,381.5	7,402.7	38.372
340	2,317.2	1,642.0	28.130	1600	11,092.5	7,915.1	38.830
360	2,446.8	1,731.9	28.501	1700	11,807.4	8,431.4	39.264
380	2,577.8	1,823.2	28.856	1800	12,526.8	8,952.2	39.675
400	2,710.2	1,915.8	29.195	1900	13,250.9	9,477.8	40.067
420	2,843.7	2,009.6	29.520	2000	13,980.1	10,008.4	40.441
440	2,978.1	2,104.3	29.833	2100	14,714.5	10,544.2	40.799
460	3,113.5	2,200.0	30.133	2200	15,454.4	11,085.5	41.143
480	3,249.4	2,296.2	20.424	2300	16,199.8	11,632.3	41.475
500	3,386.1	2,393.2	30.703	2400	16,950.6	12,184.5	41.794
520	3,523.2	2,490.6	30.972	2500	17,707.3	12,742.6	42.104
537	3,640.3	2,573.9	31.194	2600	18,469.7	13,306.4	42.403
540	3,660.9	2,588.5	31.232	2700	19,237.8	13,876.0	42.692
560	3,798.8	2,686.7	31.482	2800	20,011.8	14,451.4	42.973
580	3,937.1	2,785.3	31.724	2900	20,791.5	15,032.5	43.247
600	4,075.6	2,884.1	31.959	3000	21,576.9	15,619.3	43.514
620	4,214.3	2,983.1	32.187	3100	22,367.7	16,211.5	43.773
640	4,353.1	3,082.1	32.407	3200	23,164.1	16,809.3	44.026
660	4,492.1	3,181.4	32.621	3300	23,965.5	17,412.1	44.273
680	4,631.1	3,280.7	32.829	3400	24,771.9	18,019.9	44.513
700	4,770.2	3,380.1	33.031	3500	25,582.9	18,632.4	44.748
720	4,909.5	3,479.6	33.226	3600	26,398.5	19,249.4	44.978
740	5,048.8	3,579.2	33.417	3700	27,218.5	19,870.8	45.203
760	5,188.1	3,678.8	33.603	3800	28,042.8	20,496.5	45.423
780	5,327.6	3,778.6	33.784	3900	28,871.1	21,126.2	45.638
800	5,467.1	3,878.4	33.961	4000	29,703.5	21,760.0	45.849
820	5,606.7	3,978.3	34.134	4100	30,539.8	22,397.7	46.056
840	5,746.3	4,078.2	34.302	4200	31,379.8	23,039.2	46.257
860	5,885.9	4,178.0	34.466	4300	32,223.5	23,684.3	46.456
880	6,025.6	4,278.0	34.627	4400	33,070.9	24,333.1	46.651
900	6,165.3	4,378.0	34.784	4500	33,921.6	24,985.2	46.842
920	6,305.1	4,478.1	34.938	4600	34,775.7	25,640.7	47.030
940	6,444.9	4,578.1	35.087	4700	35,633.0	26,299.4	47.215
960	6,584.7	4,678.3	35.235	4800	36,493.4	26,961.2	47.396
980	6,724.6	4,778.4	35.379	4900	35,356.9	27,626.1	47.574
1000	6,864.5	4,878.6	35.520	5000	38,223.3	28,294.0	47.749
1100	7,564.6	5,380.1	36.188	5100	39,092.8	28,964.9	47.921
1200	8,265.8	5,882.8	36.798	5200	39,965.1	29,638.6	48.090
1300	8,968.7	6,387.1	37.360	5300	40,840.2	30,315.1	48.257

TABLE A–23E

Ideal-gas properties of water vapor, H_2O

T R	$\bar{h}$ Btu/lbmol	$\bar{u}$ Btu/lbmol	$\bar{s}°$ Btu/lbmol · R	T R	$\bar{h}$ Btu/lbmol	$\bar{u}$ Btu/lbmol	$\bar{s}°$ Btu/lbmol · R
300	2,367.6	1,771.8	40.439	1080	8,768.2	6,623.5	50.854
320	2,526.8	1,891.3	40.952	1100	8,942.0	6,757.5	51.013
340	2,686.0	2,010.8	41.435	1120	9,116.4	6,892.2	51.171
360	2,845.1	2,130.2	41.889	1140	9,291.4	7,027.5	51.325
380	3,004.4	2,249.8	42.320	1160	9,467.1	7,163.5	51.478
400	3,163.8	2,369.4	42.728	1180	9,643.4	7,300.1	51.360
420	3,323.2	2,489.1	43.117	1200	9,820.4	7,437.4	51.777
440	3,482.7	2,608.9	43.487	1220	9,998.0	7,575.2	51.925
460	3,642.3	2,728.8	43.841	1240	10,176.1	7,713.6	52.070
480	3,802.0	2,848.8	44.182	1260	10,354.9	7,852.7	52.212
500	3,962.0	2,969.1	44.508	1280	10,534.4	7,992.5	52.354
520	4,122.0	3,089.4	44.821	1300	10,714.5	8,132.9	52.494
537	4,258.0	3,191.9	45.079	1320	10,895.3	8,274.0	52.631
540	4,282.4	3,210.0	45.124	1340	11,076.6	8,415.5	52.768
560	4,442.8	3,330.7	45.415	1360	11,258.7	8,557.9	52.903
580	4,603.7	3,451.9	45.696	1380	11,441.4	8,700.9	53.037
600	4,764.7	3,573.2	45.970	1400	11,624.8	8,844.6	53.168
620	4,926.1	3,694.9	46.235	1420	11,808.8	8,988.9	53.299
640	5,087.8	3,816.8	46.492	1440	11,993.4	9,133.8	53.428
660	5,250.0	3,939.3	46.741	1460	12,178.8	9,279.4	53.556
680	5,412.5	4,062.1	46.984	1480	12,364.8	9,425.7	53.682
700	5,575.4	4,185.3	47.219	1500	12,551.4	9,572.7	53.808
720	5,738.8	4,309.0	47.450	1520	12,738.8	9,720.3	53.932
740	5,902.6	4,433.1	47.673	1540	12,926.8	9,868.6	54.055
760	6,066.9	4,557.6	47.893	1560	13,115.6	10,017.6	54.117
780	6,231.7	4,682.7	48.106	1580	13,305.0	10,167.3	54.298
800	6,396.9	4,808.2	48.316	1600	13,494.4	10,317.6	54.418
820	6,562.6	4,934.2	48.520	1620	13,685.7	10,468.6	54.535
840	6,728.9	5,060.8	48.721	1640	13,877.0	10,620.2	54.653
860	6,895.6	5,187.8	48.916	1660	14,069.2	10,772.7	54.770
880	7,062.9	5,315.3	49.109	1680	14,261.9	10,925.6	54.886
900	7,230.9	5,443.6	49.298	1700	14,455.4	11,079.4	54.999
920	7,399.4	5,572.4	49.483	1720	14,649.5	11,233.8	55.113
940	7,568.4	5,701.7	49.665	1740	14,844.3	11,388.9	55.226
960	7,738.0	5,831.6	49.843	1760	15,039.8	11,544.7	55.339
980	7,908.2	5,962.0	50.019	1780	15,236.1	11,701.2	55.449
1000	8,078.2	6,093.0	50.191	1800	15,433.0	11,858.4	55.559
1020	8,250.4	6,224.8	50.360	1820	15,630.6	12,016.3	55.668
1040	8,422.4	6,357.1	50.528	1840	15,828.7	12,174.7	55.777
1060	8,595.0	6,490.0	50.693	1860	16,027.6	12,333.9	55.884

H₂O

Ideal-gas properties of water vapor, H_2O (*Concluded*)

T R	$\bar{h}$ Btu/lbmol	$\bar{u}$ Btu/lbmol	$\bar{s}°$ Btu/lbmol·R	T R	$\bar{h}$ Btu/lbmol	$\bar{u}$ Btu/lbmol	$\bar{s}°$ Btu/lbmol·R
1900	16,428	12,654	56.097	3500	34,324	27,373	62.876
1940	16,830	12,977	56.307	3540	34,809	27,779	63.015
1980	17,235	13,303	56.514	3580	35,296	28,187	63.153
2020	17,643	13,632	56.719	3620	35,785	28,596	63.288
2060	18,054	13,963	56.920	3660	36,274	29,006	63.423
2100	18,467	14,297	57.119	3700	36,765	29,418	63.557
2140	18,883	14,633	57.315	3740	37,258	29,831	63.690
2180	19,301	14,972	57.509	3780	37,752	30,245	63.821
2220	19,722	15,313	57.701	3820	38,247	30,661	63.952
2260	20,145	15,657	57.889	3860	38,743	31,077	64.082
2300	20,571	16,003	58.077	3900	39,240	31,495	64.210
2340	20,999	16,352	58.261	3940	39,739	31,915	64.338
2380	21,429	16,703	58.445	3980	40,239	32,335	64.465
2420	21,862	17,057	58.625	4020	40,740	32,757	64.591
2460	22,298	17,413	58.803	4060	41,242	33,179	64.715
2500	22,735	17,771	58.980	4100	41,745	33,603	64.839
2540	23,175	18,131	59.155	4140	42,250	34,028	64.962
2580	23,618	18,494	59.328	4180	42,755	34,454	65.084
2620	24,062	18,859	59.500	4220	43,267	34,881	65.204
2660	24,508	19,226	59.669	4260	43,769	35,310	65.325
2700	24,957	19,595	59.837	4300	44,278	35,739	65.444
2740	25,408	19,967	60.003	4340	44,788	36,169	65.563
2780	25,861	20,340	60.167	4380	45,298	36,600	65.680
2820	26,316	20,715	60.330	4420	45,810	37,032	65.797
2860	26,773	21,093	60.490	4460	46,322	37,465	65.913
2900	27,231	21,472	60.650	4500	46,836	37,900	66.028
2940	27,692	21,853	60.809	4540	47,350	38,334	66.142
2980	28,154	22,237	60.965	4580	47,866	38,770	66.255
3020	28,619	22,621	61.120	4620	48,382	39,207	66.368
3060	29,085	23,085	61.274	4660	48,899	39,645	66.480
3100	29,553	23,397	61.426	4700	49,417	40,083	66.591
3140	30,023	23,787	61.577	4740	49,936	40,523	66.701
3180	30,494	24,179	61.727	4780	50,455	40,963	66.811
3220	30,967	24,572	61.874	4820	50,976	41,404	66.920
3260	31,442	24,968	62.022	4860	51,497	41,856	67.028
3300	31,918	25,365	62.167	4900	52,019	42,288	67.135
3340	32,396	25,763	62.312	5000	53,327	43,398	67.401
3380	32,876	26,164	62.454	5100	54,640	44,512	67.662
3420	33,357	26,565	62.597	5200	55,957	45,631	67.918
3460	33,839	26,968	62.738	5300	57,279	46,754	68.172

Enthalpy of formation, Gibbs function of formation, and absolute entropy at 77°F, 1 atm

Substance	Formula	$\bar{h}_f^\circ$ Btu/lbmol	$\bar{g}_f^\circ$ Btu/lbmol	$\bar{s}^\circ$ Btu/lbmol·R
Carbon	C(s)	0	0	1.36
Hydrogen	H$_2$(g)	0	0	31.21
Nitrogen	N$_2$(g)	0	0	45.77
Oxygen	O$_2$(g)	0	0	49.00
Carbon monoxide	CO(g)	−47,540	−59,010	47.21
Carbon dioxide	CO$_2$(g)	−169,300	−169,680	51.07
Water vapor	H$_2$O(g)	−104,040	−98,350	45.11
Water	H$_2$O(ℓ)	−122,970	−102,040	16.71
Hydrogen peroxide	H$_2$O$_2$(g)	−58,640	−45,430	55.60
Ammonia	NH$_3$(g)	−19,750	−7,140	45.97
Methane	CH$_4$(g)	−32,210	−21,860	44.49
Acetylene	C$_2$H$_2$(g)	+97,540	+87,990	48.00
Ethylene	C$_2$H$_4$(g)	+22,490	+29,306	52.54
Ethane	C$_2$H$_6$(g)	−36,420	−14,150	54.85
Propylene	C$_3$H$_6$(g)	+8,790	+26,980	63.80
Propane	C$_3$H$_8$(g)	−44,680	−10,105	64.51
n-Butane	C$_4$H$_{10}$(g)	−54,270	−6,760	74.11
n-Octane	C$_8$H$_{18}$(g)	−89,680	+7,110	111.55
n-Octane	C$_8$H$_{18}$(ℓ)	−107,530	+2,840	86.23
n-Dodecane	C$_{12}$H$_{26}$(g)	−125,190	+21,570	148.86
Benzene	C$_6$H$_6$(g)	+35,680	+55,780	64.34
Methyl alcohol	CH$_3$OH(g)	−86,540	−69,700	57.29
Methyl alcohol	CH$_3$OH(ℓ)	−102,670	−71,570	30.30
Ethyl alcohol	C$_2$H$_5$OH(g)	−101,230	−72,520	67.54
Ethyl alcohol	C$_2$H$_5$OH(ℓ)	−119,470	−75,240	38.40
Oxygen	O(g)	+107,210	+99,710	38.47
Hydrogen	H(g)	+93,780	+87,460	27.39
Nitrogen	N(g)	+203,340	+195,970	36.61
Hydroxyl	OH(g)	+16,790	+14,750	43.92

Source: From JANAF, Thermochemical Tables (Midland, MI: Dow Chemical Co., 1971), Selected Values of Chemical Thermodynamic Properties, NBS Technical Note 270-3, 1968; and API Research Project 44 (Carnegie Press, 1953).

Properties of some common fuels and hydrocarbons

Fuel (phase)	Formula	Molar mass, lbm/lbmol	Density,[1] lbm/ft^3	Enthalpy of vaporization,[2] Btu/lbm	Specific heat,[1] c_p Btu/ lbm · °F	Higher heating value,[3] Btu/lbm	Lower heating value,[3] Btu/lbm
Carbon (s)	C	12.011	125	—	0.169	14,100	14,100
Hydrogen (g)	H_2	2.016	—	—	3.44	60,970	51,600
Carbon monoxide (g)	CO	28.013	—	—	0.251	4,340	4,340
Methane (g)	CH_4	16.043	—	219	0.525	23,880	21,520
Methanol (ℓ)	CH_4O	32.042	49.3	502	0.604	9,740	8,570
Acetylene (g)	C_2H_2	26.038	—	—	0.404	21,490	20,760
Ethane (g)	C_2H_6	30.070	—	74	0.418	22,320	20,430
Ethanol (ℓ)	C_2H_6O	46.069	49.3	395	0.583	12,760	11,530
Propane (ℓ)	C_3H_8	44.097	31.2	144	0.662	21,640	19,930
Butane (ℓ)	C_4H_{10}	58.123	36.1	156	0.578	21,130	19,510
1-Pentene (ℓ)	C_5H_{10}	70.134	40.0	156	0.525	20,540	19,190
Isopentane (ℓ)	C_5H_{12}	72.150	39.1	—	0.554	20,890	19,310
Benzene (ℓ)	C_6H_6	78.114	54.7	186	0.411	17,970	17,240
Hexene (ℓ)	C_6H_{12}	84.161	42.0	169	0.439	20,430	19,090
Hexane (ℓ)	C_6H_{14}	86.177	41.2	157	0.542	20,770	19,240
Toluene (ℓ)	C_7H_8	92.141	54.1	177	0.408	18,230	17,420
Heptane (ℓ)	C_7H_{16}	100.204	42.7	157	0.535	20,680	19,180
Octane (ℓ)	C_8H_{18}	114.231	43.9	156	0.533	20,590	19,100
Decane (ℓ)	$C_{10}H_{22}$	142.285	45.6	155	0.528	20,490	19,020
Gasoline (ℓ)	$C_nH_{1.87n}$	100–110	45–49	151	0.57	20,300	18,900
Light diesel (ℓ)	$C_nH_{1.8n}$	170	49–52	116	0.53	19,800	18,600
Heavy diesel (ℓ)	$C_nH_{1.7n}$	200	51–55	99	0.45	19,600	18,400
Natural gas (g)	$C_nH_{3.8n}N_{0.1n}$	18	—	—	0.48	21,500	19,400

[1]At 1 atm and 68°F.

[2]At 77°F for liquid fuels, and 1 atm and normal boiling temperature for gaseous fuels.

[3]At 77°F. Multiply by molar mass to obtain heating values in Btu/lbmol.

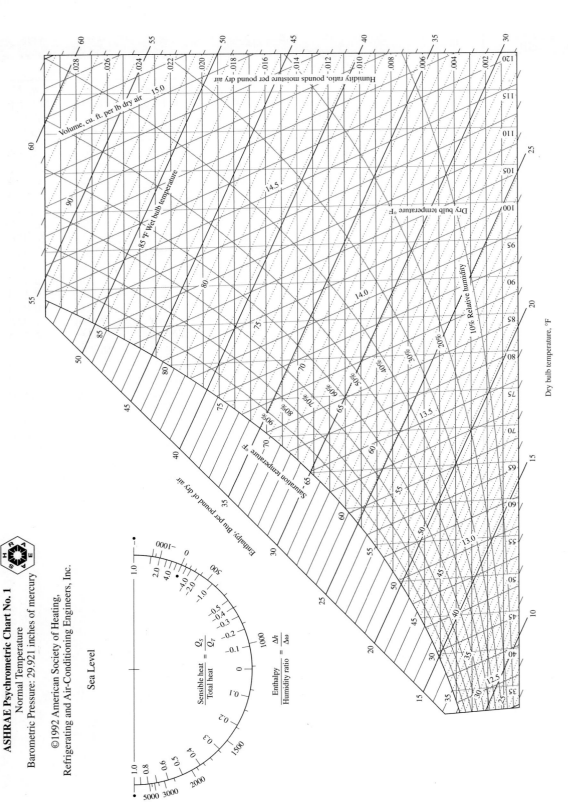

ASHRAE Psychrometric Chart No. 1
Normal Temperature
Barometric Pressure: 29.921 inches of mercury

©1992 American Society of Heating,
Refrigerating and Air-Conditioning Engineers, Inc.

Sea Level

Prepared by Center for Applied Thermodynamic Studies, University of Idaho.

FIGURE A–31E

Psychrometric chart at 1 atm total pressure.

From the American Society of Heating, Refrigerating and Air-Conditioning Engineers, Atlanta, GA: used with permission.